Practical
Pre-School

What Learn ...

ONE WEEK LOAN

Knowl   the World

ar

nce

ogy

ole Creary

About this book

This book takes a close look at one of the six areas of learning in the curriculum guidelines across the United Kingdom - Knowledge and Understanding of the World in England, Wales and Scotland, Early Experiences in Science and Technology in Northern Ireland. It focuses specifically on the science and technology aspects of the area. Another book in this series looks at the history and geography elements.

Guidance and good practice

The author explains what these elements of the area of learning consist of, what the jargon means and how it applies to the various settings in the Foundation Stage of education - children aged between three and rising six.

There are four different curriculum bodies across the United Kingdom - the Qualifications and Curriculum Authority (QCA) in England; the Curriculum and Assessment Authority for Wales (Awdurdod Cwricwlwm Ac Asesu Cymru); the Scottish Consultative Council on the Curriculum; and the Northern Ireland Council for the Curriculum Examinations and Assessment. Each has a different statement relating to the desired curriculum for young children. However, although there are some differences in terminology and some slight variations in emphasis, good practice in one country is still considered good practice in another.

As well as giving theoretical guidance - albeit in practical terms - the book also offers suggestions for activities which can be used to deliver the curriculum requirements.

Practical activities

All these activities should be considered as merging into the normal life of the early years setting. We have stressed the importance of play and how the areas of learning are linked. The activities are not prescriptive and should not be seen as tasks to complete. They are designed to be manageable and fun.

There are suggestions for 15 activities. Some are simple and straightforward activities which need few resources. Others are deliberately more challenging. Each can be used in some form with children at different stages of development.

There can be no prescriptive 'at four-and-a-half a child should be able to ...' statements and although children tend to move along a continuum of development their progress will not necessarily be steady or uniform. Any age-related guidance should be seen as what it is meant to be - a generality for guidance only.

If followed throughout the year the activities in this book cover all the science and technology Early Learning Goals (ELGs) within Knowledge and Understanding of the World. Many of the ELGs overlap and interrelate with

another. The activities therefore often fulfil more than one ELG. All the activities follow the same format. Ideas for assessment are also included.

The books in this series have been designed to be suitable for all types of settings from school reception classes to voluntary groups in church halls. You may want to adapt and change them to make them more appropriate for your group. If used in conjunction with the *Planning for Learning* series, also from Step

Forward Publishing, they should provide a basis for planned work in all aspects of the Foundation Stage of education.

Planning

A planning chart has been included for support and guidance but we would encourage you to adapt this readily to meet your own needs and circumstances.

There are seven books in this series, and although each book can be used by itself, they are designed to fit together so that the whole learning framework is covered.

The seven titles are:

❑ Personal, Social and Emotional Development

❑ Communication, Language and Literacy

❑ Mathematical Development

❑ Knowledge and Understanding of the World: Geography and History

❑ Knowledge and Understanding of the World: Science and Technology.

❑ Physical Development

❑ Creative Development

All of these books carry some activities based on common themes which, when used together, will give enough ideas for a cross-curricular topic over a half term or even a full term.

The common themes are:

❑ Seasons

❑ Water

❑ Colour

❑ All about me

❑ People who help us

All the books together provide an outline of the learning which should be taking place in the Foundation Stage.

Assessment

Each activity includes suggestions for assessment. Assessment involves two distinct activities:

❑ The gathering of information about the child's capabilities.

❑ Making a judgement based on this information.

Assessment should not take place in isolation. We assess to meet individual needs and ensure progress. The following ideas may help your assessment to be more effective.

❑ Assessment is a continuous process. It should be systematic to ensure all children are observed on a regular basis.

❑ Assessment should always start with the child. The first steps in providing appropriate provision is by sensitively observing children to identify their learning need.

❑ Assessment should not take place to see how much the child has learned but should take place to plan appropriately for future activities.

❑ You should be a participant in the assessment process, interacting and communicating with the child.

The main way of assessing the young child is through careful observation.

Observations should:

❑ Record both the positive and negative behaviour shown.

❑ Be long enough to make the child's behaviour meaningful.

❑ Record only what you see and not what you think you have seen or heard.

❑ Be clear - before you begin be sure you know what you want to observe.

❑ Be organised - plan ahead, otherwise it will not happen.

National guidelines

Each area of the United Kingdom has produced its own document outlining the expected achievements of a child by the time he or she is five. Although different in format, the expectations are broadly similar. The Scottish document gives more detail and examples of good practice than the others while the Northern Ireland document has a useful section outlining the progress that might be expected in each area of learning.

The areas of learning are also different in each document. While sometimes having the same title, the aspects of learning covered within those areas vary. For example, in the Scottish document, mathematics is included in the Knowledge and Understanding of the World section together with science and technology experiences. The Northern Ireland document puts learning about science and technology in one area (Early Experiences in Science and Technology) and Knowledge and Appreciation of the Environment in another.

The activities and ideas in this book will fit comfortably with each of the documents although the precise reference may vary from document to document for the above reasons.

A detailed analysis of the English Early Learning Goals appears on pages 9-12.

The Scottish Curriculum Framework

This is a comprehensive document and worth reading by anyone interested in the education of young children. There are five areas of learning:

❑ Emotional, Personal and Social Development

❑ Communication and Language

❑ Knowledge and Understanding of the World

❑ Expressive and Aesthetic Development

❑ Physical Development and Movement

Mathematics is included in Knowledge and Understanding of the World.

Each section has a full introduction explaining the kind of things children might do to develop their understanding and several case studies to clarify further how children's learning can be enhanced. Margin notes and questions at the end of each section make the document a useful vehicle for training activities.

Knowledge and Understanding of the World

The framework states that in developing their knowledge and understanding of the world children should learn to:

❑ develop their powers of understanding through using their senses;

❑ recognise objects by sight, sound, touch, smell and taste;

❑ ask questions, experiment, design and make and solve problems;

❑ recognise patterns, shapes and colours in the world around them;

❑ sort and categorise things into groups;

❑ understand some properties of materials, for example soft/hard, smooth/rough;

❑ understand the routines and jobs of familiar people;

❑ become familiar with the early years setting and places in the local area;

❑ become aware of everyday uses of technology and use these appropriately (scissors, waterproof clothing, fridge, bicycle);

❑ be aware of daily time sequences, and words to describe/measure time, for example their own growth, changes in the weather, trees, flowers;

❑ care for living things, for example plants, pets at home;

❑ be aware of feeling good and of the importance of hygiene, diet, exercise and personal safety;

❑ develop an appreciation of natural beauty and a sense of wonder about the world;

❑ understand and use mathematical processes such as matching, sorting, grouping, counting and measuring;

- ❏ apply these processes in solving mathematical problems;

- ❏ identify and use numbers up to ten during play experiences and counting games;

- ❏ recognise familiar shapes during play activities;

- ❏ use mathematical language appropriate to the learning situation.

This is a comprehensive but realistic list of the learning opportunities that children should have in this area of the curriculum, during their early years. It is broadly similar to the English version but giving, perhaps, a little more detail.

There is guidance on making activities relevant to the children and their surroundings. There is also emphasis on helping children to appreciate the beauty of the world and maintain the sense of awe and wonder at the scale of things.

Technology is taken in its widest form to include simple everyday things well within the experience of most children. There is no mention of computers or programmable toys.

All through the document there is a great feeling that learning should be fun and the importance of play is well recognised.

The Welsh Desirable Outcomes for Children's Learning before Compulsory School Age

The areas of learning in the Welsh document are broadly similar to those in the English version although placed in a slightly different order:

- ❏ Language, Literacy and Communication Skills

- ❏ Personal and Social Development

- ❏ Mathematical Development

- ❏ Knowledge and Understanding of the World

- ❏ Physical Development

- ❏ Creative Development

The statements concerning science and technology are mostly found in the section on Knowledge and

Understanding of the World with one or two under Physical Development. They are fairly general, giving plenty of leeway in the choice of context.

It is expected that children will begin to learn about their environment and know about the seasons and their features. Topics about the weather, growing things and seasonal change would help the children's understanding in this area.

Learning about pushing, pulling and experimenting is mentioned in the introduction to the area of Knowledge and Understanding of the World but is not highlighted as a bullet point. Children can experience pushing and pulling while playing with large toys or in movement lessons, both mentioned in the Physical Development section of the document.

There is, however, specific mention of finding out, problem-solving and decision-making; a good foundation for later investigative work. Finding out about how things work or building the tallest tower can introduce children to simple problem-solving.

It is only after having lots of experience and help in making choices about which materials or equipment to use that children will be able to begin making such choices independently.

There is reference to developing an awareness of their own bodies and their growth in the Physical Development section. Learning about their bodies and the names of the various body parts is an important aspect of a young child's learning. (Activities related to this can be found on pages 56-59. There are separate activities to do with exploring the senses on pages 32-33.)

There are several references to the use of tools, choosing materials, cutting, folding, joining, and so on, both in Knowledge and Understanding of the World and Physical Development. There is also mention of information technology as an information source.

The outcomes relevant to science and technology are:

Knowledge and Understanding of the World

The experiences that children have had by the time they are five should enable them to:

❏ talk about home and where they live;

❏ begin to understand about different places such as the countryside and the town;

❏ have a basic understanding of the seasons and their features;

❏ begin to understand the idea of time: meal times, times of the day (morning, bedtime), sequencing (yesterday, today, tomorrow);

❏ identify some kinds of workers by characteristics of work: dentist, doctor, farmer, teacher, postal worker, factory worker, mechanic;

❏ have a basic understanding of the purpose and use of money;

❏ begin to find out about outcomes, problem-solving and decision-making;

❏ begin to understand the use of a variety of information sources (for example books, television, libraries, information technology);

❏ begin to appreciate the importance of the environment;

❏ begin to understand about food and where it comes from;

❏ begin to appreciate the differences in a range of materials;

❏ make choices and select materials from a range, exploring their potential, cutting, folding, joining and comparing.

Personal and Social Development

❏ understand that all living things should be treated with care, respect and concern.

Physical Development

❏ have awareness of their own bodies and growth;

❏ handle small tools and objects with increasing control and for appropriate purposes (for example: pencils, paintbrushes).

The Northern Ireland Curricular Guidance for Pre-School Education

In Northern Ireland there are seven areas of learning rather than six, the extra one being specifically concerned with children learning to appreciate the environment. Many of the statements in this section may be found in the other documents, scattered through the different areas of learning. Putting them together in their own section raises the profile and gives prominence to this area of learning.

❏ Personal, Social and Emotional Development

❏ Physical Development

❏ Creative/Aesthetic Development

❏ Language Development

❏ Early Mathematical Experiences

❏ Early Experiences in Science and Technology

❏ Knowledge and Appreciation of the Environment

The bullet points outlining the aspects of learning that the children should experience within each area also offer some detail and examples of what the statement means. However, these are only examples and children will need a wider range of activities to consolidate their learning. This book should help you with this.

The document also states clearly the advantages of having an adult working with children. It talks about how, by commenting, questioning or offering additional material, the adult can extend the children's learning and expectations. Many of the activities and ideas in this book include the sort of questions that you might ask children to extend their thinking.

Early Experiences in Science and Technology

The NI guidance states that children need opportunities to:

❑ observe and explore, for example, in water play when they explore the properties of water and observe how different objects behave in water;

❑ use their senses, for example, in sand play when they feel the texture of dry and damp sand and make comparisons or when they identify sounds such as the telephone ringing, blocks falling and birds singing;

❑ explore, for example, in creative/aesthetic play when they work with malleable materials such as dough and clay, becoming aware of how these materials behave when poked, rolled, squashed and pulled;

❑ observe and respect living things, handling them with care and sensitivity, for example, by helping to attend to plants and helping to keep the nature/interest table fresh and attractive;

❑ make models, for example, in construction play when they assemble, rearrange and build blocks and other materials, observing that carefully stacked blocks are less likely to fall than those that are stacked haphazardly and that a broad surface of blocks gives a better base for building;

❑ put things together in a variety of ways, for example, in creative or construction play when they make models with materials, both natural and man-made, sticking, cutting, folding and, on occasions, taking things apart;

❑ learn about themselves by talking with adults and listening to appropriate stories, rhymes and songs.

Knowledge and Appreciation of the Environment

To help them develop knowledge and understanding of the environment children should have opportunities, individually or in groups, to:

❑ experiment with a wide variety of play materials. Through talking with adults and other children, they learn the names of materials and equipment and observe how these behave. They develop an awareness of space as they help to tidy away equipment. They become familiar with some positional and directional words;

❑ talk about topics which arise naturally from the children's own experience, for example, holidays, festive seasons and birthdays;

❑ explore items on the nature/interest table, for example, photographs of events that took place during the year, plants at different stages of development and natural materials such as sheep's wool or shells;

❑ talk about the weather and the seasons at appropriate times of the year;

❑ talk about themselves, for example where they live, the members of their extended family and events in their lives both past and present;

❑ listen to stories and rhymes which have some reference to the past;

❑ use their senses to explore the immediate inside and outside environment;

❑ play with simple floor maps and small vehicles, discussing road safety when appropriate;

❑ learn about their pre-school setting, for example, the name of the setting and the people who work in it, the names, function and position of different rooms, and the name of the school to which they will transfer;

❑ play with materials associated with different places and occupations, such as the seaside, the farm, the fire station and talk about related ideas with adults;

❑ talk about the work of some of the people in the local community, for example, the shopkeeper and the dentist.

❑ take some responsibility for caring for their own environment, and become aware of environmental issues such as litter, road safety and the use of paper and bottle banks.

The area of learning explained

We live in an increasingly complex world with science and technology playing an ever greater role. Things Granny only dreamed of are now part of everyday life. Granny spent all day over a wash tub and mangle - now we just put the dirty clothes in a metal box, press a button and go and do something else. Illnesses that were once life threatening now respond to a single dose of antibiotic. We travel distances in hours that would, not so long ago, have taken weeks.

Much of this change has come about because people were curious and wondered, 'What would happen if ... ?' Or they resolved to find a better way of doing something. They raised questions or they solved problems. This is what we need to encourage our young children to do and it's never too soon to start.

Science is all about finding out about the world and our place in it. Technology is about using and applying scientific concepts to solve problems and make life better, anything from synthesising a new drug or extending the shelf-life of a loaf of bread to providing clean water for a remote village or sending people to the moon.

We need to offer children a wide range of experiences that will help them to develop the skills and curiosity that will enable them to find out about themselves and their surroundings. We need to encourage them to use all their senses. Remember that, although you may have looked inside a flower hundreds of times or built more tall towers than you've had hot dinners, it

may be the first time that child has seen it or done it. Join in the 'awe and wonder' and be ready to capitalise on the enthusiasm. Asking the right question at the right time is the key to encouraging a child's thinking.

Sometimes the awe and wonder works the other way. Children have no fear of computers, knobs or buttons. While we might hesitate and think twice about pressing anything in case the whole lot disappears, children have no such inhibitions. They will quite happily press everything in sight just to see what happens. We need to help children develop these random explorations into more systematic and logical investigations.

Different answers *haven't used*

We obviously don't expect children at this stage to carry out full scientific investigations or fair tests but we can help them begin to understand the relationship between cause and effect. We can encourage them to make predictions about what they think might happen and then carry on to find out if the prediction was correct. However, it is important that children learn to accept, as soon as possible, that if something different happens, they are not wrong. We really need some words other than 'right' or 'wrong' in this context. Children come to us with the clear picture that everything is either 'right' or 'wrong', but in scientific investigations there may be several different answers to the same question. In technology, different people may come up with different answers to the same problem, but each

may be equally valid. Children who are told that their prediction is wrong may become reluctant to offer their ideas in case they are wrong again. Just try to celebrate the surprise of the unexpected.

The stages in learning

Children go through different stages in their learning. Young children are at the experiential stage, soaking up new ideas like sponges. They need to have a wide range of experiences so that they can approach ideas from different angles and gradually build up concepts.

They then need to be encouraged to describe their experiences and observations. Because they have not yet developed the necessary language, some children may find this difficult but, with encouragement, the sentences will get longer and the vocabulary richer. At first it will be a straightforward, simple report but as the children increase in confidence, start asking them if they can give a reason for what has happened. The reason may not be very scientific at first - or even accurate - but it is the beginning of the next stage in the children's learning.

This stage is being able to explain what you have experienced or observed. Most children will be at secondary school before they can give scientifically accurate explanations about forces so don't worry if your five-year-olds aren't forthcoming. Explanations should become increasingly detailed and accurate as the children progress.

The Early Learning Goals

Knowledge and Understanding of the World

In this area of learning, children are developing the skills, knowledge and understanding that help them to make sense of the world. This forms the foundation for later work in science, technology, history, geography, design and technology and information and communication technology.

By the end of the Foundation Stage, most children will be able to:

1. Investigate objects and materials by using all of their senses as appropriate.

Children need to be encouraged, and in some cases taught, to use all their available senses to find out about themselves and their surroundings. They need to be taught to see what they are looking at. Ask questions to encourage them to look for detail such as:

❏ Does everybody have the same colour eyes?

❏ Are those birds/leaves both the same? How are they different? Why are they different?

Developing a child's listening skills seems to be one of the major challenges of education in today's noisy world. We need to teach children to discriminate and really listen to the sounds that are important, not only to make better observations but also for their own safety. Investigating the sound made by a drum or tambourine may be exciting but the sound of a boiling kettle or an approaching car should warn of possible danger.

Touch is an important sense allowing us to explore shape, texture, flexibility and temperature. For children with hearing or sight difficulties it may be

their main window on the world. Activities with feely bags and known items such as stones, shells, pine cones or made objects such as combs, spoons, pencils or rubbers, can progress into similar activities but with less familiar items and textures.

Alongside this developing awareness, children also need to acquire the language to describe their

observations. Try to introduce them to the correct scientific or technical language from the beginning. Small children usually love big words - just think how many of them can name dinosaurs for you. Use the correct terminology but always add a definition to help the child's understanding. For example: 'The chocolate in my hand has melted, it isn't solid anymore, it's gone runny, it's changed into a liquid.'

Taste is an exciting and, usually, pleasurable sense to explore but also has health and safety issues. With small

children everything seems to gravitate to their mouths and it is important for them to learn that this is not necessarily a good idea, especially with unknown substances. Teaching them not to taste strange things unless told by a responsible adult that it is safe to do so may be easier than persuading them not to lick the mixing spoon or bowl when baking. (Tasting anything with raw egg in is to be discouraged because of the risk of salmonella poisoning.)

Smell is the most evocative of our senses and can stimulate memories long consigned to the back burner. It is also a great one for exercising language skills. Ban 'nice' or 'nasty' and ask the children for words to describe what they smell. Does it remind them of anything? I smell coal dust and I'm immediately taken back to my childhood, watching the coalman tip coal into the cellar. Most smells are specific or can only be described by relating them to something else. How do you describe the smell of an orange or new-mown hay? Smells can also warn of danger - burning, smoke, bad meat, and so on.

2. Find out about, and identify some features of, living things, objects and events they observe.

At this stage, you don't have to worry too much about children being able to identify the particular species of ant they are observing or the geological formation of a lump of rock but they do need to be able to begin to make general statements about objects or events. They should be able to tell the difference between a flower and a leaf or a hammer and a screwdriver. Naming the parts of their own bodies will help them to identify similar parts in other animals. A few pot plants or vases of flowers in the room not only enhance the surroundings but also give children the opportunity to observe the different features of plants. Dismantle an old torch to find out how it works or look at a bicycle to find out why the wheels go round when you turn the pedals. Thematic displays can stimulate a child's curiosity especially if they are interactive rather than purely visual. They may need more maintenance but are well worth the effort.

Describing events such as blowing the biggest bubble, watching ants moving their eggs to safety or recounting how they melted chocolate to make rice crispie cookies, can all help children develop both language and speaking and listening skills.

3. Look closely at similarities, differences, patterns and change.

This is closely related to the last statement. As children's language and observation skills develop they are able to describe objects and events in more detail. Given two objects, a ball and an orange, they will probably tell you that one is orange the other red, you can eat one but not the other, you play with the ball but not the orange, and so on, giving differences between the two objects. They probably won't tell you that they are both round or spherical. You may have to question them to find out the similarities they have observed. It is important that they begin to see that many animals have the same features - eyes, legs, tails, that most tools have handles of some kind, that cars and lorries all have wheels, that trees have trunks and leaves, and so on, since this is the beginning of classification.

Children may learn to recognise patterns of shape and colour, and even make their own at quite an early stage, but they will need help to recognise patterns in events or happenings. Day and night is a simple one with which to begin and so is seasons (a three-year-old doesn't have

much experience of them to draw on but five-year-olds should begin to see the annual pattern). Watching frogspawn change into frogs or eggs hatch into chicks helps to establish the concept of life-cycles, as does following the birth and growth of a baby brother or sister and relating this to their own experience of growing up. Roll cars down a slope to see which goes furthest. If each child tries the same three cars and the red one is always best, that is a simple pattern. When out looking for minibeasts, they may notice that woodlice are always found where it is dark and damp. Can they find any similar patterns?

4. Ask questions about why things happen and how things work.

There is so much in the world today that we just take for granted.

It is not necessary, or even desirable, to know how everything works. I'm quite happy as long as my washing machine works when I press the appropriate buttons. I don't really have to know exactly what all the electrical connections are and how they operate. And yet I am intrigued by how a bird manages to carry out such a wonderful feat of engineering as building a nest, using only a beak and a foot. Why does bread rise and then bake to a crusty, golden brown? What do all the cables at the back of the computer do or why doesn't my bike work if the chain comes off? Some of these are questions to which I may never get an answer, others I can read about, ask about or simply find out by trial and error, but the important thing is that the questions have been asked. We need to stimulate children's curiosity, encourage them to ask questions and help them to find the answers (or at least some of them).

A battery, small bulb and a couple of wires may set a child to thinking how a torch works. Magnets are a great favourite and usually raise lots of questions: What will it stick to? Why won't the two red ends stick together? Which picks up most paper-clips? Some of these questions can be answered at this stage but others will need to wait until the child has a better understanding of particle physics! If you do find yourself at a loss, admit it and ask the children if they have any ideas. Value their answers and explore their ideas with them. You may need to explain that the real answer is very complicated and they will learn about it later.

Remember, it is not only the questions that the children ask that are important but the questions you ask of them. Try to keep questions open-ended so that the answer cannot be a straight 'yes' or 'no'. It is sometimes a good idea to plan the sort of questions you might ask during an activity in order to get the children thinking.

Questions such as:

❑ What are we trying to find out?

❑ How do you think we could do it?

❑ What do you think will happen?

❑ What equipment do you think we might need?

❑ Do we need to measure or count anything?

❑ How will we measure it?

❑ How will we remember what we did?

❑ What will be the best way of telling or showing other people what we did?

❑ What did we find out?

❑ Could we have done it a different/better way?

These are questions that might be asked in other areas of learning not just science and technology. They may also be asked at any age or stage - the answers should become more sophisticated as the children progress.

Encourage all the adults working with the children to use similar questions whenever possible. A copy of the list is useful as an aide memoire for volunteer helpers. Obviously, the very youngest children may need a little more direction until they have gained some experience with tools and equipment but, even so, questions such as 'Which spoon do you think will be best for stirring the pudding mix?' or 'Where do you think is the best place to look for snails?' all encourage children to think for themselves and gradually become more independent in their learning.

5. Build and construct with a wide range of objects, selecting appropriate resources, and adapting their work where necessary.

What self-respecting nursery or reception class would be without its junk box? Boxes and bottles ready to be turned into anything from a house to a rocket (possibly within the same model, depending when you ask!). If not properly managed, however, the wonderful resource of found materials could quickly become just a heap of junk that threatens to take over. I find plastic dustbins (clearly labelled to avoid mistakes!), a good, cheap way of keeping materials organised and sorted - round things in one, boxes in another, sheet materials in another, depending how much room you have. Lids keep the contents from straying and if the bin is full, then you don't need more of that type for a while.

Use paper and card to make simple models or pop-up cards for special occasions. Designing, cutting and sticking using a variety of materials helps children to develop aesthetic as well as manipulative skills. Give children experience of as wide a range of materials and techniques as possible so that later they will be able to choose for themselves the materials and process appropriate to the task in

hand. At first, children need to be offered a fairly limited range of materials for each task or you may find that they are overwhelmed. But gradually, you can increase the choice and encourage children to choose the materials and technique they want to use. Ideally, children should know where everything is kept and be able to find and take what they want. Equally important, they should learn to put it away properly when they have finished.

Construction toys are a perennial favourite, particularly with boys. Don't be afraid to introduce positive discrimination sometimes to make sure that the girls also have a turn. Look, too, at the kits you have. Are they really geared towards boys? Do they only make vehicles or guns and swords? There are some kits on the market now that are much more girl-friendly and allow for a much wider range of models to be made.

As well as free play with construction toys that allows children to use their imaginations, occasionally set a task for the children to complete using a particular kit (or mixture of kits if you can manage the sorting out afterwards). For example, build a tower exactly as tall as the table, make a windmill with sails that turn or a lorry that has six sets of wheels. This can encourage children to begin to develop their problem-solving skills as well as their imaginations.

Playdough, Plasticine and clay are great fun. Clay can be messy but nothing else feels quite like it when it squidges through your fingers. I prefer playdough to Plasticine - some Plasticine can be hard and seems to break into small pieces that won't stick back together again. Playdough is cheap and versatile, according to which recipe you use. It can be simply used as an experience in shaping, rolling and kneading or, with a different recipe, baked and made into a more permanent record of the children's work.

There are several good no-bake clays available to buy. They tend to be expensive, but for a special project are well worth considering.

6. Select the tools and techniques they need to shape, assemble and join the materials they are using.

Do make sure that any tools the children use are up to the job in hand. Scissors that don't cut are frustrating and more dangerous than a sharp pair since the children try everything to make them cut. It is perhaps a good idea to have a set of scissors that are kept just for fabric work so that they don't get covered in glue and lose their edge.

The same applies for knives. You obviously don't want to give small children razor-sharp, pointed kitchen knives but they do need one that is sharp enough to cut up vegetables if that is the task. It is important to teach children to use any tools properly and safely. If they learn to use them in a safe and secure setting and are made aware of any possible dangers then that is a life skill.

Encourage the children to experiment with different types of glue, paste or sticky tape to fix their models. I find 35mm film canisters excellent for keeping PVA type glues in. The tight fitting lids stop the glue from drying out but are still easy to get off and because the glue is in a small pot, the children tend to be more sparing in its use. If they tip it over then less is spilled - no bad thing on a tight budget! The canisters fit nicely into the bottom of an egg box which also provides a resting place for the sticky

spreaders. A small stapler or paper-clips to fix thin card or paper might be appropriate for some children to try.

Only when they have had lots of help and experience using different tools and materials will children be able to make sensible, informed choices for themselves about the best tools and materials for a particular project.

7. Find out about and identify the uses of everyday technology and use information and communication technology and programmable toys to support their learning.

Technology touches almost every aspect of our lives today. Young children have never experienced life without aeroplanes, television or cash points while some of us are still trying to get to grips with these 'new-fangled' machines. It is quite illuminating to sit at the end of a busy day and think of all the technology that has impinged on you during that time. Did you use 'advanced formula' toothpaste from a special dispensing pack to clean your teeth? Did you have cornflakes (produced in a factory) and semi-

skimmed milk (advanced dairy technology) for breakfast? What about the shape of the tea bag you used for your cuppa? Did you set the timer on the washing machine or video recorder before you drove to work? Will you pop a ready meal from the freezer into the microwave when you get home?

Ask the children to think about the things they use during their day. Where do they think they were made and how, in general terms, do they think they work? Do they realise that video machines have tiny computers in them? Many children have small, hand-held games machines. Do they appreciate that these are small computers? Can they use a mouse or keyboard with a PC or program a simple robot such as Pixie? Can they use a tape recorder to record their work and play it back? Do they sometimes draw pictures on acetate so that they can use the overhead projector to make it really big?

Equipment

You can do a great deal of science and technology with found materials or things from your kitchen cupboards but it is worth investing in a few quality items, many of which will also be useful in other areas of the curriculum.

Good quality magnifiers help children to look more closely. The type on a stand that has a fixed focus are particularly good for younger children since they are usually quite large, giving a good field of view and leaving hands free. Children can then progress to using hand lenses. These also need to be of reasonable quality and size and you will need to teach the children how to use them properly. Plastic ones are preferable (and cheaper) to glass at this stage, especially since the glass ones are often contained within a metal band screwed into a handle. Children soon find that they can be unscrewed and taken apart with potentially disastrous results. However, the plastic ones do get scratched and should be treated as semi-consumable with, perhaps, a rolling programme for replacement.

Plastic mirrors are also useful and safe. Try taking the backing off only one side to begin with. Tape over the edges with masking or sticky tape to keep the backing on the reverse. When the first side has become scratched remove the tape and backing to give you a little more wear, but again mirrors should be inspected regularly and replaced when necessary. Give them a good wash in soapy water occasionally - it works wonders.

Magnets need to be reasonably strong. Some of the best are ceramic bar magnets encased in plastic. They are bright and attractive and tend not to lose their magnetism when dropped as many metal ones do. You can also get giant magnets in the shape of big horseshoes or even elephants. While they are great fun, they are not so versatile in investigations as the more traditional bar magnets and some of them are almost too big for little hands.

A few simple electrical components are good for helping children to learn about cause and effect. A battery, a couple of wires with crocodile clips on each end and a bulb in a bulb holder will provide hours of fun. There are components available where the connections are magnetic. Although these were principally designed for children with special needs, I have found them useful with young children still developing their manipulative skills, who find crocodile clips difficult to manage.

Plastic fish tanks are a useful addition to the science store. They can be used, obviously, for fish or tadpoles but also make good temporary homes for snails or spiders or see-through containers for watching things float or sink.

Plastic trays - the sort used for cat litter - are also extremely useful. They can be used as collecting trays for minibeasts when on safari or pond creatures when pond dipping (white trays are best for this). They act as drip trays when blowing bubbles or finding out which materials are waterproof if the water tray is otherwise occupied. Activities can be put in them for giving out and collecting quickly.

I have already mentioned the need for good, sharp scissors but a small collection of other tools is useful. Mini-hacksaws with comfortable handles will deal with most things at this stage although a small tenon saw is a useful standby for the occasional tougher piece of timber. A couple of small hammers, a pair of pliers and a small hand drill should satisfy most would-be carpenters at this stage. Some kind of vice for holding things steady while they are drilled or sawn is also useful.

How much high-tech equipment you have depends on your budget and storage facilities. Tape recorders are affordable these days and have many uses across all the areas of learning.

A camera is a useful tool to record children's work in progress or such events as outings or celebrations. Films for a Polaroid camera may appear to be more expensive but exposures can be used one at a time, you don't have to use the whole film and the results are immediate. If you have a computer then think about investing in a digital camera. The pictures can be shown on the screen and stored in the computer and you never have to buy another film or pay for processing.

A TV and video or CD-ROM, used wisely, can provide the children with pictures and images outside their experience - jungles, deserts, strange and wonderful creatures. If you are lucky enough to have access to a video camera this can be an excellent way of recording the trip to the farm, supermarket or wherever. The children will play it back until the tape wears out so that they can see themselves and relive the experiences.

Computers are becoming more and more a part of everyday life and many of your children will already have experience of using them. If you have one, make sure that all children become familiar with using it and that it is not just regarded as a reward for being good or finishing first! If you don't have a computer, don't feel pressurised into buying such an expensive piece of equipment if you think it is inappropriate for your needs.

Programmable toys are available in various guises but, while good in the home, they often don't withstand the rigours of the nursery or school. Pixie is a sturdy, box-shaped robot suitable for this age group. It can be decorated and made into a variety of different things to fit in with your topic.

Links with other areas of learning

In the early stages of learning it is often impossible to separate out specific subjects or areas of learning, because each is heavily reliant on the others. Children cannot talk about what they have observed unless they have the language to describe it. They cannot tell you how far a toy car has travelled if they don't have at least the beginnings of mathematical ideas about distance.

Personal, Social and Emotional Development

In developing their Knowledge and Understanding of the World, children are finding out about the world, how things work and why things happen. It is important that they begin to realise that they, too, are a part of the world and that they have an affect on their environment and the other people they live, work and play with. If they drop litter, someone else has to pick it up. If they charge about on their bicycle without looking where they are going, someone may get hurt. Sharing a bag of sweets may make someone smile. Showing someone the caterpillar you found makes it twice as exciting.

Talking about things they have done or observed gives children an opportunity to share their ideas with others. They begin to realise that other people, too, have ideas and that these ideas are worth considering and may add to their own understanding. By valuing children's ideas, however far-fetched they may seem, you can help them to grow in confidence.

Gentle questioning and suggestion can steer them back on to the right track without destroying their self-esteem.

Carrying out an investigation often means working with other people. Rolling cars to see how far they go is much more fun done as a race or competition than on your own. Again, this will give children the opportunity to share ideas and talk about the task in hand. Explaining what has happened or what they have found out helps children to order their thoughts.

Reporting back to the class can give them the opportunity to gain confidence in speaking to a larger audience.

As children progress they will take a greater role in planning how to carry out an investigation. They will have ideas about the equipment and resources that they wish to use. However, they will only do this if they have had lots of opportunities to play with and experience the things beforehand. Plastic droppers and syringes are good for measuring small quantities but children will not use them as tools unless they have played with them first. If you buy a new music centre, you don't really use it until you have pressed all the buttons and twiddled all the knobs to find out exactly what it can do.

Children should also develop their responsibility for getting equipment out and putting it away. This has implications for classroom management. Obviously, some equipment needs to be kept more securely, but children should be able to fetch and use a magnifier, if they need one, or a metre rule or measuring jug.

Finding out about the world is exciting, inspiring awe and wonder - and lots and lots of questions. Why doesn't a spider trip over its legs? How does a bird know how to build a nest? How does a tin-opener work? Where does the wind come from? A child, who may not be able to sit still for a story, may sit for hours watching a snail crawl up the side of a tank. Making a picture book about the snail to take home, or to show at sharing time, may provide the motivation to produce the finished article.

A great deal of the work about 'me' or 'myself' is also linked with Personal, Social and Emotional Development: learning to share and consider other people's needs, learning to work together and listen to the ideas of others, knowing that we have different feelings and that we can affect the feelings of others, understanding that friends are important.

It also links with learning about keeping ourselves clean and healthy. Children need to become independent in dealing with personal hygiene as soon as possible. Washing hands after using the toilet and always before handling food should become second nature, but we all know how much reminding has to take place. Explain why cleanliness is so important, that germs can pass from one person to another, particularly on food.

Communication, Language and Literacy

Talking about the things they have done or found out gives children many opportunities for developing their language skills. Activities such as describing the contents of a feely bag or the similarities and differences between two objects can boost vocabulary.

Recounting how they made some cakes or how they put the wheels on a model can help children to organise their thoughts and put events into a proper sequence. For example: 'First we glued the boxes together, next we made holes for the axles and pushed the sticks through and then we put the wheels on the ends of the axles.' Children need to develop the ability to think sequentially in order to plan investigations and projects. Baking a cake or decorating the bedroom are both completed more easily if we have the skills to plan the tasks involved in a logical order. It is no good adding the egg once the cake is in the oven or painting the ceiling after putting down the new carpet!

Some activities demand specialist language. Children should use the correct language, whenever possible, in order to reduce the risk of acquiring misconceptions. Children love big words so don't be frightened of them. If you are using a new word, always add a definition. For example: 'The window is transparent, we can see through it' or, 'Look! The sugar has dissolved. We can't see it any more. It has disappeared into the water.' You may need to add the definition each time you use the word for some time.

Wanting to find out more about the snail you found or the fossil Grandad gave you is great motivation for delving into a book. It is important for children to realise that they can get information from different sources such as books, CDs or even the Internet. The more enthusiastic the children become about a topic the greater the motivation to find out more so it is important to build up a library of suitable books appropriate to the current interest. Encourage parents to take their children to the local library to find books about a special interest and perhaps bring them along to share with the rest of the group.

Making a book about a special interest may encourage the first steps in writing. Diagrams and observational drawings give children plenty of opportunities for labelling. Older children might begin to write lists of the equipment they need for an investigation or some of the steps in their planning. They could write captions for photographs to explain, for example, what they saw at the zoo.

Mathematical Development

There are close links between Mathematical Development and Knowledge and Understanding of the World, particularly the science and technology aspects. Counting fingers and toes, the number of objects in a set or the spots on a ladybird provide contexts for the children to develop their counting skills.

Much of the early language children use to describe things is mathematical. Children may refer to size or shape when comparing objects and use words such as 'round' and 'bigger than' or 'smaller than', 'long' and 'thin' or 'short' and 'fatter than' to describe them. They explore 3-d shapes when using building blocks or choosing boxes to make their models. When talking about the distance travelled by

toy cars they may use language such as, 'The red car went further than the blue one but not as far as the yellow one.'

Taking measurements is an important part of collecting data in science investigations or constructing models in technology. Measurements of length may be in a concrete way to begin with - comparing lengths of string or ribbon, for example, to compare how far different vehicles travelled. Children will then use handspans, cubes or other non-standard measures before learning to use standard measures. They can also order the cars in order of distance travelled so that they have first, second, third and so on.

Playing in the water tray enables children to understand the language of capacity or volume - full, empty, enough, too much - and this can be put into context when measuring ingredients for recipes (two cups of flour, one teaspoonful of salt, and so on).

To find out which is the biggest apple young children might guess and then weigh them in their hands to decide which is the heavier. Some children might try balancing them against each other in a set of scales while older children could balance them against cubes or beads. Some cubes have the mass of one gram each that then helps the children when they progress to using standard measures. Cooking activities may provide a context for introducing standard measures.

It is important that children have experience of measuring things in different ways and using different equipment so that, later, they are able to choose the appropriate method of collecting data. Equally important is the way in which they present that data. Even very young children can add their picture to a pictogram to show the distribution of eye or hair colour. A simple block

graph or bar chart may help children to compare distances travelled more easily than a set of numbers.

Physical Development

Projects about 'Ourselves' are usually closely linked to children's physical development.

Learning about their bodies and thinking about how they move helps them grow in confidence. They may compare the things they can do now with the things they could do when they were babies. Increasing control and co-ordination allows them to become more aware of how they move in relation to others.

Children need to understand that taking exercise is an important aspect of keeping healthy. If they learn to enjoy physical activities while young then they are more likely to carry them on into adult life.

PE and movement sessions also give children opportunities to experience forces such as pushing and pulling. Similar experiences can be afforded

through outside play. Throwing and catching not only helps to develop hand-eye co-ordination but also to sow early ideas about forces.

Many of the activities in science or technology help children to develop manipulative skills - moulding playdough or pastry, rolling out and cutting, using tools such as scissors or hammers with increasing dexterity. Learning to use a plastic dropper or syringe for measuring small quantities of liquid demands a fair amount of fine motor control. For this reason children need to have lots of opportunities to play with such things so that when they need to use them they can do so with increasing accuracy.

Creative Development

Many activities in the area of technology have strong links with the creative area of the curriculum and many science activities, at this stage, are often recorded in a creative way.

Self-portraits are a good way of recording details about 'me', while observational drawings or paintings can motivate children to look carefully at things they find. Clay or playdough models can record explorations of malleable materials while patterns with hammer and nails show work with more resistant materials.

Exploring colour and texture, taste and smell is an important part of any topic on the senses. Investigating sound may be done as a topic in its own right or included within work on the senses.

Cooking activities allow children to experience more subtle textures, for example when rubbing in pastry or kneading bread. They can practise measuring and counting skills. They can begin to appreciate that materials can change or alter. Sometimes those changes can be reversed, as in turning juice into ice to make lollies, and then watching lollies melt and turn back into juice. Sometimes the changes are permanent, as in baking a cake. Designing a sandwich or decorating a cake helps children to appreciate the aesthetic aspects of presenting food and how the look and smell of food can affect our appetites.

Making music is a way of exploring sound. By exploring the different sounds they can make by clapping, stamping, shouting, whispering, and so on, children learn more about their own bodies and what they can do. Listening to a variety of music can help them experience different moods, for example, dancing to a lively jig or disco beat, or sitting quietly, listening to a more gentle piece. Some children with hearing difficulties may still be able to respond to the beat or resonance of different instruments.

Children can explore the quality of sounds by making their own simple instruments such as shakers or elastic band guitars. Banging on a saucepan with a wooden spoon makes a different sound from doing the same thing with a metal spoon. Like much science at this stage, children will not be able to give or understand the scientific explanations. However, they need a rich variety of experiences in order to begin to develop ideas that will, later, enable them to understand more fully.

The importance of play

If we think of science as finding out about the world and everything in it, then very young children probably do more science than anyone else. They are constantly exploring and finding out. Technology gives them tools to enhance their explorations and hopefully stimulates their curiosity even further to find out how things work and eventually to make or invent things for themselves.

In their early years, children learn mostly through play, and this is particularly true for science and technology. Playing with bricks helps develop early ideas about shape and structure. Cutting out, sticking and pasting or playing with dough helps children to explore materials and develop an awareness of tools. While this type of activity is often directed, and needs to be if children are to move forward in their thinking, we must not forget that children need time to consolidate their ideas and sometimes look at them from different angles. They need time to play without an adult breathing down their necks.

Opportunities for play

An important role for the adult is to provide opportunities and situations in which children can play and explore safely. Create interest corners or tables, make space for building or rolling toy cars, provide sand and water trays, perhaps a piece of ground to dig or a work bench with simple tools.

Tools and equipment is an area where the importance of play can sometimes be overlooked. We are often concerned about the element of

danger that some tools hold but children still need that time to play and practise for themselves. Small plastic droppers or syringes are useful for measuring small quantities but children need to have played with them, discovered their possibilities and become confident in handling them before they can use them for a

particular purpose. Saws and scissors need a great deal of practice to make perfect. Explain the dangers and supervise closely at first but then leave the children to use them how they want.

The water tray and the sand tray are great play areas where children can try

out lots of ideas about science and technology. A little scene-setting can help children to extend their ideas. By putting a particular selection of toys in the sand or water you can guide children's play in a specific direction. Containers of different size and shape develop ideas about capacity and volume. Jugs, waterwheels and plastic piping all help children think about how water flows. Providing wet sand and dry sand, side by side, helps children to make comparisons as they try to dig, mould and pour the same, but different, material.

Science corners

A small corner or table on which you can put objects of interest or introduce new ideas can be useful. Here children can play with things such as magnets, discover some of their properties and think about what they have found out. When you then come to do planned activities with magnets, the children will have ideas and knowledge to share. Play after these activities will give the children opportunities to explore further and consolidate their ideas. I always find that putting a battery, bulb and a couple of wires out in this way is a good way of introducing the idea of electricity.

On some occasions you might have a 'How does it work?' table. Old clocks, cameras or torches that can be taken to bits or such things as rotary whisks and garlic presses that have easy-to-see mechanisms, help children to question how things work.

A quiet corner can provide somewhere for children to sit and think about their ideas. We don't necessarily think of this type of activity as play, but not all children want to tear around all the time. A quiet corner, perhaps with books or pictures about the current topic, will give some children a little breathing space and allow them time to gather their thoughts.

Role play

The home corner provides lots of opportunities for children to test their ideas. A hospital setting can help children learn about themselves and develop ideas about caring. Why do people go to hospital? Could we avoid getting hurt in accidents? Who is there to help us? Dressing-up clothes for doctor and nurse are often provided, but what about props for the ambulance man or paramedic, the laboratory technician or cleaner?

A café situation can encourage children to think about food and hygiene. Where does the food come from? What should we always do before handling food? How do we keep food fresh? Why should we keep the café clean and tidy? Provide a hand towel and soap and other cleaning materials (clean, empty bottles to pretend). Label one cupboard as a fridge if you don't have one as part of the home corner and encourage children to use it for keeping food cool. Provide boxes or covers for the sandwiches on display. Why do we need to keep food cool or covered? Why do we need to wash our hands?

A little adult intervention can be useful in helping to move play on. The right question at the right time can help focus children's thinking. Observing children playing and listening to their conversations (sometimes with themselves) is also a good way of assessing their understanding in a particular area. A child wiping the table down between customers or 'washing' their hands before making a sandwich is obviously developing ideas about the need for cleanliness when handling food.

Outside play

Outside play provides many opportunities for children to learn about forces in action. Children will learn to ride a bike or a scooter. They will discover how to make it go where they want. They will learn how to stop and start again. They will push or pull carts and wagons and find that they are more difficult to move when full. They won't be thinking about forces but they will be gathering experiences and information to help them to develop concepts about forces and energy.

Climbing frames allow children to explore how they can move and what their bodies are capable of. There is an element of danger and daring-do to climb to the very top, something that may be missing in many children's lives these days. Many of us will remember playing out in the street or disappearing into the fields until teatime. In many areas this is no longer possible or advisable so children are cheated of adventure. Climbing to the top of the frame or the slide may recompense to some degree.

Try to have an area where there is enough space for children to play with bricks or construction toys - room to build roadways along which to 'brrrmm' a car or experiment with bridges. A piece of carpet helps to deaden the noise as the tower falls over for the nth time. But as they stack them back up again, children are learning about structures and finding out how things fit together. They may be learning to share and co-operate in a larger project to solve problems. Well-timed intervention is necessary but sometimes we might be a little too anxious to interfere and forget all the learning that is happening through play.

Pushing and pulling

Forces are, perhaps, one of the more difficult areas of science to understand, although forces surround us all the time and have a profound impact on our lives. Young children may not understand about forces but they can experience and begin to describe what is happening when forces are acting. They can begin to think about cause and effect, for example: 'If I want that pushchair to move, I've got to push it', 'If I drop my ball, it will fall to the floor', 'If I want to have fun on the swing someone will have to push me'.

Children at this stage do not need to identify any particular forces but they do need to know and use words such as pull, push, twist, fast, slow and stop and start. Be careful not to use words such as pressure and power when talking about forces in order to avoid misconceptions and confusion later on.

Learning objectives

❑ To know that pushes or pulls can make things move;

❑ To know that pushes and pulls are types of force;

❑ To help children begin to understand about cause and effect;

❑ To use a force to change the direction of an object;

❑ To experience materials changing shape;

❑ To experience friction during play.

Forces can start something moving, speed it up, slow it down, stop it, change its direction or change its shape. Most forces can be described in the simple terms of a push or a pull.

squeak!

Playing with the big, outdoor toys provides opportunities for children to experience forces in action. As they are playing, ask questions to make them think about what they are doing. What is happening as a result of their actions? For example, what do you have to do to make your bicycle or scooter move? Get them to think about how they have to push down on the pedals to make their bike move or push their foot against the ground to get their scooter moving. What happens if they turn the handlebars or put on the brakes? Any activity that involves movement must involve forces.

Where do you start?

Physical development provides opportunities for children to experience forces acting upon themselves. Ask the children to work with a partner and sit on the floor, facing each other with legs slightly bent and feet touching.

❑ What can you feel if you push with your feet?

❑ Try pushing with one foot and then the other. Take it in turns to push and relax. What do you feel?

Next ask the children to stand up facing their partner and try a similar pushing activity but this time using their hands.

❑ What happens if only one partner pushes?

❑ What happens if they both push at the same time?

❑ What happens if one partner pushes harder than the other?

Talk about a push being a force. A bigger push is a bigger force. Forces have size (magnitude) and direction and always act in pairs. If there is a push in one direction then the object being pushed will provide an opposing force in the opposite direction. Pushing against their partner helps children to experience this opposing force as their partner pushes back.

Push-along toys help children to realise that forces have direction. Think of a child pushing a trolley or other wheeled toy. Usually the trolley is light enough for the child's push to be the bigger of the two main forces and so the trolley moves forward, in the direction of the push. If they push more on one side than the other then the trolley will change direction. A heavier object would have a greater opposing force and would therefore need a bigger push to move it.

When children are playing on ride-on toys, ask them to decide whether they are pushing or pulling. For example, they push the pedals to make a tricycle move, they push the ground with a foot to move a scooter, they push the pedals in a pedal car, someone pushes to get them moving on a swing.

Think about activities that the children are going to be involved in. Can you identify forces they will be using? What questions can you ask to draw their attention to what they are doing and make them think about it?

At the dough table, encourage children to think about what they do to change the shape of their dough. Do they pull it or push it? Roll it (a push and a pull) to make a long sausage? Roll it with a rolling pin to make a pancake?

What do they push or pull when they're getting dressed? They pull on socks and trousers; pull up a zip; pull their jumpers over their heads and push their feet into shoes.

Fun and games

Ball games provide lots of opportunities for experiencing forces. A throw or a kick is a kind of push. The bigger the push the further the ball goes. If you throw or kick a ball against a wall it will bounce back again. The wall provides a force that stops the ball and then changes its direction. This is perhaps better felt by using a bat to push the ball back to a partner. Don't ask for explanations at this stage, just provide the experiences and the language.

Early Learning Goals

These activities will help you work towards the following goals:

❑ Find out about, and identify some features of, living things, objects and events they observe.

❑ Look closely at similarities, differences, patterns and change.

❑ Ask questions about why things happen and how things work.

❑ Build and construct with a wide range of objects, selecting appropriate resources, and adapting their work where necessary.

❑ Select the tools and techniques they need to shape, assemble and join the materials they are using.

jumbo plastic straw

wheel pushed on to dowel

Stick straw to model and thread dowel through. Push wheels on to dowel.

use hole punch to make hole for axle

thin wooden dowel or paper sticks

Make sure opposite holes line up. Use dowel, paper sticks or straws for axles. Cotton reels make good wheels. Hold them on with a bead or twisted elastic bands.

elastic band

bead

Forces can:

❏ Start something moving:

a push, a pull or gravity

❏ Make a moving thing go faster:

increasing the push or pull

❏ Make a moving thing change direction:

hit a ball with a bat

❏ Make a moving thing slow down:

put the brakes on

❏ Make a moving thing stop:

catch the ball

❏ Temporarily change the shape of an object:

roll out the dough

❏ Permanently change the shape of an object:

crush the garlic!

Games such as skittles or bowls provide opportunities for simple investigations. How hard do you have to roll the ball? Does it make a difference if the skittles are big and heavy or small and light? Does the size or weight of the ball matter?

You can make a simple set of skittles from empty plastic drinks bottles. Have fun playing the game and counting how many are knocked down each time. Ideas of fairness can be introduced by having a starting line and using the same ball each time. *(Experiential stage)*

Weight the bottles by putting a little sand or water in each one. Play the game again. Ask the children to describe what is happening. Is it easier

or harder to knock the new skittles down? Experiment by putting increasing amounts of sand and water in the bottles. Is easier or harder to knock them over? Encourage the children to think about how hard they are throwing the ball each time. *(Descriptive stage)*

Ask the children to explain why they think the full ones are harder to knock down or why it is easier with a heavier ball. *(Explanatory stage)*

Slowing down and stopping

The force that makes things slow down or stop is friction. Without it things would slide everywhere, objects would not stay where we put them. It is the friction between our feet and the ground that enables us to walk.

Children may have experienced a lack of friction when trying to walk on an icy surface or on the wet floor at the swimming pool. Some of them may have tried roller-skating.

Find a large, sturdy box or use a wooden stage block. Sit a child in it (or on it) and let other children try pulling or pushing them across the floor. Try doing it on different surfaces such as carpet and tiles.

❏ Which is easier? Why?

The children might tell you that it is easier on the tiles because 'the bits on the carpet get in the way' - an early start to understanding friction. You could then encourage them to think about how they could make it easier to move.

❏ Why do they think things have wheels?

Try putting the box on a pair of roller skates or make some rollers from broom handles or rounders posts.

❏ Does that make it easier or more difficult to move?

Investigate which is the best surface for rolling cars the furthest. Having decided which surface is good, encourage the children to make their own vehicles either from construction kits or from recycled materials.

Children's own models often fail to move satisfactorily because of the friction they have built in. A wheel is a device for overcoming friction and therefore has to move as freely as possible if it is to work properly. Axle holders help (see diagrams).

Investigating gravity

Gravity is, perhaps, one of the first forces that children investigate. They soon seem to learn that every time they throw something out of their highchair it goes down and lands on the floor, whether it be a rattle or rice pudding!

They may also have experienced climbing up the steps and sliding down a slide.

❏ Why, when they jump up, do they always come down again?

❏ Why, if you put a ball at the top of a slope, does it always roll down?

❏ Why is it harder to ride your bike up a slope than on the flat and why do you go faster down hill?

Encourage the children to think about why things happen and to talk about their ideas and describe what they observe. After all, no one really knows what gravity is but without it we would have no weight and all drift off into space.

So that's gravity!

Stories

Meg's Car Helen Nicholl and Jan Pienkowski (Picture Puffin).

Mr Gumpy's Motor Car John Burningham (Picture Puffin).

Mrs Mopple's Washing Line Annita Hewett (Picture Puffin).

Postman Pat to the Rescue John Cunliffe (a Hippo Book from Scholastic).

Old Bear Jane Hissey (Beaver).

Poems and songs

'See-saw, Marjorie Daw'

'Jack and Jill'

'The wheels on the bus go round and round'

'Row, row, row your boat'

What's cooking?

Being able to feed oneself is a basic life skill and it is never too soon to begin learning how to do this in an exciting but nutritious way. Cooking activities also provide lots of opportunities to explore materials and how they change. Many recipes require access to a cooker of some kind but there are lots of things that you can make without.

Learning objectives

❑ To learn that cooking and preparing food can be fun;

❑ To understand the basic rules of hygiene;

❑ To learn to use simple kitchen equipment safely;

❑ To know about changes that occur during cooking;

❑ To begin to measure using non-standard and standard measures;

❑ To follow instructions.

Cooking activities are also a good vehicle for reinforcing messages about health and hygiene. For all the activities make sure that you have a clean surface on which to work, aprons for the children and warm, soapy water for frequent hand-washing. Although it is almost tradition to lick spoons and bowls for the last of the cake mix, do be careful if the recipe contains raw egg. There may be a risk of salmonella and this is obviously best avoided.

Preparing food provides wonderful opportunities for sharing and experiencing aspects of different cultures. Invite parents in to share a favourite recipe or talk about a particular festival and the food associated with it. Perhaps you could make a batch of cakes or biscuits and invite some of the senior citizens in the community to come and try them along with a cup of tea.

Planning food for a birthday party or a picnic provides opportunities to talk about why we need to eat fruit and vegetables and not just chips and chocolate. Helping to prepare the mid-session snacks and taking turns to serve each other can help children to learn to share, show consideration for each other and gain independence.

Tools of the trade

If you have access to a cooker then there is virtually no limit to the recipes you can try. A microwave is almost as good but cakes and biscuits tend to be rather pale and uninteresting. A small hot plate will enable you to boil eggs, make soups, jams, custards, and so on. An electric kettle means jellies and chocolate crispies are on the menu. Safety is of paramount importance whatever you are using.

Children should be taught the rules about not touching hot things and they should always be closely supervised during cooking activities. There are, of course, lots of things that you can do without heat. A refrigerator is a bonus.

Wherever possible, avoid using glass or pottery containers. Try to introduce children to a variety of utensils such as spoons, forks, whisks of various sorts, fish slices, rolling pins and cutters so that, as they gain experience, they can begin to select the appropriate tool for the task in hand. Children should be taught to use knives properly and safely. If they are preparing fruit and vegetables then they need a knife that is up to the job. They don't need a razor-sharp butcher's knife but they do need one that is sharp enough to cut without them needing to use undue pressure. A blunt knife can trap and bruise small fingers as the children press harder and harder in their frustration. We need to teach children

how to work safely and sensibly within a safe and secure environment, so that they are better equipped to meet the dangers of life outside.

What does it feel like?

Whatever you are cooking or preparing, allow a little extra of each ingredient so that the children can explore the feel, texture and, perhaps, the taste of it, before it is mixed or changed in some way. How does fat feel compared to flour or sugar? What are the more subtle differences between ordinary flour and cornflour? How does butter or margarine change when it is whisked together with sugar? Or butter change when we heat it gently? How do we change the shape of a lump of dough or make biscuits the right shape?

Cold cookery

Peppermint creams

You will need a packet of ready-made fondant icing, peppermint flavouring and food colouring (optional). Give each child a very small piece to taste.

❑ What does the paste feel like?

❑ What can you smell?

❑ What does it taste like?

❑ Why do you think it goes sticky when you hold it?

Divide the icing into smaller pieces that the children can handle. Add a few drops of peppermint flavouring to each piece (depending how strong you want them to be). Then knead each piece thoroughly to mix in the flavouring. You can also add a few drops of food colouring at this stage if you wish. A little cornflour sprinkled on the work surface and fingers will help to stop things getting too sticky.

❑ What can you smell now?

❑ Does it feel different?

❑ Has the taste changed?

(Tasting has to be well regulated or there is a danger of never getting to the final product!)

Form the sweets simply by rolling into small, marble-sized balls or roll out the paste and use different shaped small cutters. Alternatively, roll the paste into a sausage shape and cut into small slices. Ask the children what they are doing to change the shape of the paste. Use silver balls, small pieces of glace cherry or angelica to decorate and leave to dry. This is probably the hardest part for the children!

Salads

Salads of all kinds are fun to prepare and you can use almost anything you have to hand. They are especially good if you can use ingredients that you have grown yourself such as lettuce, cress or radishes or even some cherry tomatoes but otherwise, take a trip to the local greengrocer or supermarket to choose the ingredients. If you book the trip in advance, you may even get someone to give you a guided tour and tell you about the different things on offer.

Do the children know the names of any of the vegetables? Have they eaten them before? How could they sort them? Which part do we eat?

Show children how to wash the vegetables and talk about why it is necessary to do so. When you cut the vegetables up, look for seeds or patterns inside. Is the pattern the same if you cut it the other way? What do they think the seeds would grow into?

Make sure that the children are working at a comfortable height while they are cutting up the vegetables, and that they are working on a suitable surface.

Fruit salad

Fruit salad may well be more popular than a green salad and it can be great fun to try out the different exotic fruits now available. Again, take a trip to the supermarket if you have one nearby or bring in a selection of fruit for the children to see. Apples, oranges, pears and bananas may well be familiar from snack times but what about pineapple, mango or star fruit? Price may prohibit a really wide range of fruit for the salad but try and introduce one or two unusual fruits at each session. Which fruits do we have to peel? How many can they name?

What shapes or patterns do they see when you cut them in half? Can they find any seeds? Which fruits are soft and which crunchy?

If you feel slightly more adventurous, try making pasta salads. The pasta can be pre-cooked and mixed with various chopped vegetables, tinned fish such as tuna and mayonnaise. Check the dietary requirements of the children before offering any meat or fish.

Sandwiches

Sandwiches are fun to make if you have never spread a slice of bread before. Choose fillings to suit everyone's taste. Simple spreads or jams are perhaps the easiest things to start off with and give practice in spreading.

Getting warmer

Jelly

Jelly is a favourite with most children. You need a supply of hot water (an electric kettle) and in hot weather access to a fridge is helpful for the jellies to set properly. You may have to wait until the next day for the finished results. Gelatine is not acceptable to some vegetarians but you can buy jellies based on agar, which is derived from seaweed.

Melting and dissolving are two words that children (and adults) often use interchangeably. They actually belong to two different processes and children should always be encouraged to use the correct word from as early as possible.

Melting occurs when heat is applied to a substance and causes it to change its state from a solid into a liquid, for example ice to water, ice-cream to liquid, ice lollies to juice, chocolate to that lovely mess that gets everywhere!

Dissolving is when one substance dissolves (or the children may say disappears) in another, for example sugar in tea, bath crystals in the bath water, jelly crystals in water. The colour of the liquid may change but it should be clear. Using a thick, black pen, draw a smiley face slightly smaller than the bottom of the container you are using. If you can see the face clearly through the liquid, then the substance has dissolved, if you can't see it, then it hasn't. Clear plastic, disposable party glasses are ideal for this sort of activity.

Children can each make their own individual jelly using one or two cubes of jelly in a cup together with the appropriate amount of hot (not boiling) water. Ask them to watch

carefully and describe what is happening.

❑ What is happening to the edges of the cube?

❑ Does it seem to dissolve faster if they stir?

❑ How do they know it has all gone?

❑ How has the water changed?

Leave the jelly somewhere cool to set but check regularly to see what changes are taking place.

Once the children have experienced making jelly in the usual way then you can begin to investigate. Try giving some children hot water in their cups and others cold.

❑ Whose jelly dissolves first?

❑ Why?

❑ Does it make a difference how much water you use?

❑ Does it still dissolve if you only use a little water?

❑ Does it still set if you use a lot of water?

❑ Do all colours dissolve at the same rate?

Put two different coloured cubes in a cup and see which one dissolves first. (I found that black cherry dissolves quicker than strawberry, but that might just be the brand I was using - there's another investigation!)

Chocolate crispy cakes

Chocolate is a good material for demonstrating melting. Give each child a small piece and ask what happens if they hold the chocolate in their hand. (Have soap and water ready!)

❑ Why do you think the chocolate melts?

❑ What happens when you put it in your mouth? Why?

❑ Can you think of anything else that melts when you hold it in your hand or put it in your mouth?

The children may think of other sweets or ice-lollies but try and help the children to see the link between heating the material and it melting.

Chocolate crispy cakes are fun to make and again you only need access to hot water.

Break a bar of chocolate into small pieces and place in a bowl. Keep a piece of chocolate to one side. Put the bowl into a bigger bowl of hot water and stir until the chocolate has all melted. Compare the melted, liquid chocolate to the solid piece.

❑ How has it changed?

❑ Why has the chocolate melted?

❑ Has the taste changed?

Using a big spoon, stir in as many cornflakes or rice crispies as the chocolate will take. You can add a little dried fruit or glace cherries if you wish. Spoon the mixture into paper cases and leave to set.

❑ Why has the chocolate gone hard again?

❑ What would happen if the crispy cakes were warmed up?

Activities such as these help children begin to understand that some changes are only temporary and can easily be reversed.

Getting hotter

Fairy cakes

In all cooking activities we are looking at changes in materials, usually caused by temperature. Sponge cakes are easy to make and the changes quite dramatic. Unlike the melting and setting of chocolate, the changes that occur when cakes are cooked are permanent and not reversible.

You will need a little extra of each ingredient for the children to explore.

> You will need:
>
> 100g margarine
>
> 100g sugar
>
> 2 eggs
>
> 100g self-raising flour
>
> 12-15 paper cake cases
>
> (Halve or double the quantities according to the number of cakes you want.)

Give each child a small amount of each, except the egg, on a paper plate.

❑ What does each one feel like?

❑ How are they the same?

❑ How are they different?

Compare the sharp grittiness of sugar to the softness of flour. How do these compare to the greasy margarine? Use a magnifier to look more closely at the flour and sugar.

Break one of the eggs into a saucer and look carefully.

❑ Can you name the two main parts?

❑ How are they different?

Let the children feel the stickiness of the egg but make sure they don't lick their fingers afterwards.

Write down all the words that the children can think of to describe the different ingredients and use them together with empty wrappers/cartons to make a display.

Mix the margarine and sugar together. Use a wooden spoon and pass the bowl round the group so that each child gets a turn at mixing. Don't use too large a bowl or the children will be chasing the ingredients round rather than mixing them. They will find it easier to mix if you allow the margarine to soften a little first and place the bowl on a folded tea towel to stop it slipping.

❑ How are the ingredients changing as you mix them?

❑ How is the colour changing?

❑ Can you still see the sugar?

❑ What about the shape of the mixture?

Beat the mixture until it is light and fluffy. A little adult help may be needed here.

Beat the eggs in a separate bowl. Why not experiment and mix one egg with a fork and the other with a small balloon whisk? Which works best? Why?

❑ What has happened to the two different parts of the egg?

❑ Why are there so many bubbles?

❑ What is in the bubbles?

❑ Why do we need bubbles in a cake?

Add the beaten eggs to the sugar and margarine a little at a time and beat again.

❑ How is the mixture changing now?

❑ What does it smell like?

Sift the flour, add it to the mixture and gently fold it in.

Put a teaspoon full of mixture into each baking case and bake in a fairly hot oven. Keep one cake uncooked so that you can compare with a cooked one.

If you have a microwave oven you can watch the cakes rise through the glass door, but the cakes will not turn a golden colour when cooked.

❑ When the cakes are cooked, how have they changed?

❑ What colour are they now?

❑ What about the smell?

❑ What do they look like inside? (Use a magnifier.)

❑ How is that different from the uncooked mixture?

❑ Where do you think the bubbles from the egg went?

❑ Could we get the ingredients

back to how they were when we started?

❑ How do they taste?

Gingerbread men

This is one of my favourite recipes to make with the children since it involves melting, kneading, rolling and cutting.

Look carefully at all the ingredients and feel each one. Taste them but be careful not to try the egg. Keep a little of each to compare with the cooked gingerbread.

> You will need:
>
> 200g plain flour
>
> half a teaspoon bicarbonate of soda
>
> 1 heaped teaspoon ground ginger
>
> 50g butter or margarine
>
> 75g brown sugar
>
> 1 tablespoon golden syrup
>
> 1 egg - beaten
>
> glace cherries, currants and icing to decorate

Sieve the dry ingredients together into a mixing bowl.

❑ Why do we do this?

❑ What difference does it make?

Gently melt the margarine and sugar together in a saucepan until the sugar has melted. Do not allow to boil.

❑ How are the ingredients changing?

❑ What can you smell?

Mix together with the dry ingredients and the beaten egg to form a soft dough. Make sure it is cool and knead the dough lightly on a floured board.

❑ What does it feel like?

Use a rolling pin to roll out the dough about 0.5 cm thick. Cut into gingerbread men shapes or any shape you wish. Use a fish slice to transfer them to a well greased baking tray. Decorate with currants and cherries and bake at 180ºC (350º F) or gas Mark 4 for about 15 minutes.

Carefully remove to a cooling tray and allow to cool thoroughly.

❑ How have the gingerbread men changed? (Compare with the raw ingredients.)

❑ What has made them change?

❑ Can we get the separate ingredients back again?

Vegetable soup

This is another of my favourites. You can use almost any vegetables you can find and it provides a wonderful opportunity for introducing some unusual vegetables.

Present the children with a variety of different vegetables. Good ones to use include cabbage, carrots, potatoes, onions, leeks, celery, parsnips, mushrooms, tomatoes, swede, aubergines and peppers.

Encourage the children to look closely at each one. What colour is it? What does it feel like? Does it have a smell?

How could you sort them? Some children will need to be given the criteria but others may be able to think of their own ways to sort and you can play the game of trying to guess the criterion they have chosen. Try sorting for shape, colour, which part of the plant we eat, whether we peel it, whether it grows above or below ground, and so on. Beware of potatoes and onions! We eat the leaves of onions, the roots are those thin strands

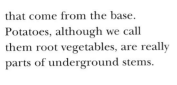

that come from the base. Potatoes, although we call them root vegetables, are really parts of underground stems.

Having looked closely at the outside, cut each vegetable in half and look again. If you have two of each, cut each in a different plane so that you can see the different patterns in, for example, an onion or a carrot. You could use one half to make some prints as a record of the children's observations but make sure you keep this activity well away from the cooking area.

Now prepare the vegetables for cooking. You need to wash them all, but do any need peeling? There are a variety of peelers available and most of them are reasonably safe for children to use. If hard vegetables such as swede or carrot are cut into long fingers, the children can then chop them into smaller pieces more easily, ready for the pot. They will need a reasonably sharp knife. Use this as an opportunity to teach them the safe way to handle knives.

Taste the raw vegetables. Which do they like best? Which is crunchiest? Keep a small piece of each so that you can compare the raw with the cooked vegetables.

Put all the chopped vegetables into a large pan and cover with water. You can add a couple of vegetable stock cubes for a little extra flavour. Simmer the soup until the vegetables are soft. This will vary depending on how much you are making but will probably be about half an hour or so.

When it is ready, allow it to cool a little and then put a small amount on a

saucer. Can the children identify any of the original vegetables? How do they compare with the raw bits you kept? How have they changed? Are they still crunchy? Has the colour changed? (Swede is interesting. While most vegetables stay the same or get paler, swede goes a deeper orange.)

Enjoy the soup as a mid-session snack or for lunch.

There are lots of other recipes that you can make but do make sure that you try them yourself before trying them with the children. Some things will be governed by the amount of time you have. Bread is wonderful to make but needs time to rise and prove so is a little difficult if you have a short session. Pancakes are quick and always popular. Encourage the children to design their own toppings or fillings. Making biscuits or jam tarts can provide practice in rolling, cutting and counting as well as measuring out ingredients.

Have lots of fun cooking, but at the same time encourage the children to think about the changes that are taking place as they mix and cook.

Story

The Magic Porridge Pot Alan MacDonald (Ladybird).

Traditional tales

'The Gingerbread Man'

'The Enormous Pancake'

(from various publishers)

Traditional poems

'Pat-a-cake, pat-a-cake'

'One potato, two potato'

Poems

'Boiling an Egg' Stanley Cook (The Oxford Treasury).

Software

My First Incredible, Amazing Dictionary (Dorling Kindersley).

Assessment

Can children describe what they see, feel, smell or taste?

Take note of those children using new words and extending their vocabulary. Look for children using scientific words such as 'melt' and 'dissolve' in the correct context.

Watch carefully how the children measure ingredients or use the equipment provided. How much help do they need? Some children may be able to make suggestions about the equipment to use.

Most children will be able to describe changes but some may understand that when some things change it is impossible to get the original materials back again.

Growing plants

Plants are an important part of our world. They are the only living things that can make their own food and animals rely on them for their food source. They absorb carbon dioxide and produce oxygen through the process of photosynthesis. Forests play an important part in recycling fresh water. They provide the raw materials for many medicines as well as habitats for innumerable species. What a bleak landscape we would have without them.

Learning objectives

❑ To appreciate the variety of plants;

❑ To know that plants are important in our lives;

❑ To recognise a few common plants;

❑ To look for similarities and differences;

❑ To know that plants grow.

Getting started

Go out and look for all the different plants you can find in your area. (You may need to point out that trees and grass are plants.)

❑ How are the plants different?

❑ Do they all have flowers?

❑ Where are the flowers on trees?

❑ Are leaves all the same shape or colour?

❑ How many different ones can you find?

Stick five or six small pieces of different coloured paper or material to the bottom of a white tray. Can the children find a leaf or flower the same colour? Older children could use paint shade cards (available from DIY stores) and see how many shades they can match. Make sure that the colours you offer can be matched.

Encourage children not to pick wild flowers randomly or tear leaves from trees. One of anything is usually enough. It is always sad to see discarded bunches of bluebells or cowslips lying by the path. Most wildflowers do not last well inside and are much better left where everyone can enjoy them. It is also illegal to pick some rarer species so it is best, perhaps, to learn to enjoy all of them in their natural habitat. It is never too early to think about conservation.

Planting seeds

Growing a plant from seed is a satisfying experience and quite wonderful if you have never done it before. Use a magnifier to look carefully at a variety of seeds such as mustard and cress, beans, French marigold or dandelion.

❑ Are they all the same?

❑ How are they different?

❑ What do you think they will grow into?

❑ How could you find out?

Look for the seeds inside plums, pears and apples. Seeds from citrus fruits germinate well and will grow into

Early Learning Goals

These activities will help you to work towards the following goals:

❑ Find out about, and identify some features of, living things, objects and events they observe.

❑ Look closely at similarities, differences, patterns and change.

reasonable plants but are unlikely to produce fruit.

Choose seeds with care. Some of the most spectacular are the most poisonous. Use this opportunity to reinforce the message about never eating seeds or berries unless told that it is safe to do so. Make a collection of seeds that we can eat - nuts, wheat, popcorn. (Making popcorn is fun and easy. You can make it in the microwave but I don't think this is as spectacular or as satisfying as the pan on the stove method.)

If space is a problem, use empty 35mm film canisters as tiny plant pots. (Most photographic processing shops will be only too glad to save the empty canisters for you.) Punch a hole in the bottom with a nail, for drainage, and keep them together in an empty, shallow ice-cream tub. Transplant the new seedlings as they get too big for the pots. This gives an opportunity to look at the roots and see how they have grown. Although the plants need light to produce healthy growth, avoid putting them in direct sunlight on a window sill where they may fry during the day and freeze overnight.

Seeds such as French marigold germinate quite quickly and will produce small bushy plants that can be carried home. If started off early enough, some may even produce seed before the summer holidays so that children can see the full life-cycle from seed back to seed again.

If you have space for a small garden, try growing a few vegetables. Radishes grow quite quickly and are fairly reliable. Lettuce and spring onions take up little space. Sowing the seeds and watching for the first green shoots is so exciting!

If you have no garden area, an old sink, big tub or growbag can make a useful substitute. Try some cherry tomatoes in a growbag - they will grow really well outside against a sunny wall, or inside in a light and airy spot. You can get some varieties, such as Tumbler, that will even grow in a hanging basket. They need lots of water so arrangements for weekends and holidays have to be considered. A wigwam of canes in a tub will support a crop of runner beans and provide opportunities for measuring and counting.

Try growing a potato in a large tub or bucket. Fill the bucket about half full of compost and plant the potato in it. As the leaves begin to show through, cover it with more compost, leaving just the tips of the leaves showing. Do this two or three times more until the bucket is full. In a couple of months or so you will be able to tip the whole thing out on to a plastic sheet and find the buried treasure - lots of little potatoes! The longer you leave it the bigger the potatoes will get. (Beware! The last one I tipped out had an ant's nest in the bottom that turned out to be more exciting than the potatoes!)

You may be able to make contact with a local allotment association and arrange for the children to visit a plot and see a wider range of things growing or, in some areas, a market garden. Many garden centres allow visits from well-supervised parties. Don't just turn up though - do make an appointment.

Transform the home corner

Turn the home corner into a garden centre for a while. Use a piece of trellis as a screen and decorate it with a trailing plant or empty seed packets. Play matching games with empty seed packets. Have some old seed catalogues and simple picture books about plants that the manager can use if asked for advice.

Sorting and matching

Seed trays and plant pots are excellent for sorting and matching but make sure that you sort them yourself before asking the children to do it. The variety of plant pots is amazing: different sizes and colours, differing numbers of holes in the bottom arranged in different patterns. Make sure that there are not too many different types to start with or the children will just be confused. They can begin sorting according to colour or size then, as they learn to count, they can sort according to the number of holes. Encourage children to choose their own criteria and explain why they have sorted in that particular way.

Useful books

Be Safe (ASE Publications, College Lane, Hatfield, Herts AL10 9AA). Contains useful guidance including lists of poisonous plants.

Stories

Meg's Veg Helen Nicoll and Jan Pienkowski (Mammoth).

Mouse Finds a Seed Nicola Moon and Anthony Morris (Pavilion).

Jasper's Beanstalk Nick Butterworth and Mick Inkpen (Hodder).

Rachel's Roses Karen Christensen (Barefoot Books).

Poems

'A spike of green' Barbara Baker; 'Little seeds' Else Holmelund Minarik. Both from *The Walker Book of Read Aloud Rhymes for the Very Young*.

Assessment

Ask the children to name the different parts of a pot plant - leaf, flower, and stem. Where are the roots? Some children might be able to label a simple picture or diagram.

Most children will know that seeds grow into new plants and some may understand that different seeds grow into different plants.

Note those who can name some common plants such as daisy, buttercup and daffodil. Most should be able to identify tree, grass or flower.

Children should know that we eat plants or parts of plants but that it is not safe to eat things we don't recognise.

Exploring the senses

Exploring the senses provides some wonderful opportunities for language development. It is difficult to describe what you see or hear, what you smell or taste or what different textures feel like, without the appropriate vocabulary. Children will obviously use the words they have but there will be many opportunities to introduce them to new words.

Learning objectives

❑ To know that they have senses that will help them find out about the world;

❑ To learn the names of these senses;

❑ To learn to use these senses to make observations;

❑ To extend their vocabulary.

Sight

Colour plays an important part in our lives and often one of the first things we teach children is to recognise and name the colours. Make collections and displays of different colours and invite the children to contribute items from home. Paint pictures or make finger paintings in the appropriate colours. Choose matching colours from a magazine or fabrics to make collage pictures. Have a blue day when everyone comes dressed in blue. Sort and match beads or counters in sets of different colours.

Shape is another criterion often used for sorting and children need to learn to recognise simple mathematical shapes. It is often by their shape that we recognise objects. We recognise a tree because it is tree shaped, a ball because it is ball shaped, but we need to make more detailed observations to know what kind of tree it is or what kind of ball. Question children carefully to encourage them to develop their observational skills, for example: 'That is a tall tree. Is it the same as the one over there?' 'How do you know?' 'Is the shape the same?' 'Are the leaves the same shape?' 'Is the trunk/bark different?'

Or, given a set of different balls such as beach, tennis, ping-pong, football, rubber: 'Bring me the football. How do you know that is the football?' 'What makes it different from the other balls?'

Children should also be introduced to simple magnifiers. Stand magnifiers are good for very young children since they are usually of a reasonable size and any object put under it is automatically in focus. At a later stage a hand lens may be more appropriate but children need to be taught to use these properly.

Play games that require children to describe things without naming them. They can describe colour, shape and any other attributes but may not use the name of the object. The others in the group have to guess what is being described.

Children with visual impairment may still be able to distinguish light and dark and even recognise some colour. They may rely more on other senses to make their observations. If a child has difficulty in learning colours it may be worth suggesting that they are checked for colour blindness.

Touch

Although we have nerve endings all over our bodies, there are particular concentrations at our finger tips and mouths.

Provide children with a selection of different materials and help them to describe what they feel like. It is better, if you can, to use a piece of the material rather than an object made from it. This helps the children to concentrate on the properties of the material rather than the properties of the object. Help the children to think of as many words as possible to describe the material. Is it bendy (flexible) or stiff (rigid)? Is it hard or soft, cold or warm, wet or dry? It is worth making a collection of materials such as a stone, a piece of wood, sponge, plastic, a lump of glass, and so on. A piece of lava has an interesting texture or, if you can't get hold of that, invest in a foot scrubber from the chemist that has a similar scratchy sort of texture.

When children first begin to sort materials or objects they need to be able to allocate things to just two sets. Rough or smooth is a fairly standard starting point but make sure that the things you give them to sort are either clearly one or the other, not somewhere in between. At a later stage

Early Learning Goals

These activities will help you to work towards the following goal:

❑ Investigate objects and materials by using all of their senses as appropriate.

children should be able to put a small number of things or materials in order from rough to smooth. Use three or four different grades of sandpaper stuck to small pieces of wood to make a permanent resource for this activity.

Although children may have learned to recognise some shapes by sight, can they recognise them by feel? Feely bags are easy to make and may be used in several different activities. Make or find a traditional small shoe bag but thread elastic through the top rather than cord. It should fit fairly snugly round the wrist so that there is no peeping but still be big enough to get different objects through. When children have explored two or three objects or materials by sight and touch, hide them all, but put one in the feely bag. Can the children guess what it is? Alternatively can they describe it so that the others in the group can guess what it is? Put all three objects or materials in the bag, name one and ask the child to find it. If you are working with very young children, you may need to begin with just two different objects or materials.

Don't be afraid to experiment with textures. Cold, cooked spaghetti in water can be interesting, especially if explored when blindfolded. Add some lemon or peppermint flavouring to give another, unexpected, dimension.

Make sure that the children are well protected and that soap and water is handy and let them explore cooking oil on a plate or cooking fat or margarine. Do this when making cakes or pastry. Feel how they change when rubbed into the flour.

Hearing

There is so much noise in our environment that it is not surprising that most of us have learned to switch off and only hear what we want to. However, we do need to teach children that it is important to listen. We sometimes need to listen to

instructions so that we know what to do. Listening to a story can be great fun. Alarm bells or sirens may warn us of danger. Some children may have problems with hearing so it is always best to check if you suspect a problem.

It is difficult to find a really quiet spot in a pre-school setting, but try and find a quiet-ish spot and get the children to sit with their eyes closed. Can they tell you what is happening around them, in the next room, outside on the road? How do they know? What are the clues?

Even very young children these days seem to have their own personal stereos and spend periods of time wearing headphones. Many of these do have a volume regulator but it is never too soon to start dropping hints about the danger of very loud sounds and the damage that they can do. Many children will complain about noises such as pneumatic drills, big lorries or loud fire bells but may not realise that loud music, playing directly into their ears over a period of time, can also have harmful effects later in life. Talk about why people using drills or other noisy equipment need to wear ear defenders.

Taste

Taste is perhaps one of the most pleasurable of our senses. Children quickly develop likes and dislikes and may be quite conservative in trying anything new. Others will eat anything. Children need to learn that it is not safe to taste unknown substances unless a responsible adult has told them that it is safe to do so.

Use favourite tastes as a context for making simple charts or pictograms. Try identifying some familiar tastes while blindfolded. Do fruit gums or Smarties all taste the same or can you identify the different colours just by taste? How much does colour influence our taste? Try putting a little blue food colouring into some mashed potato

and see which the children prefer. Introduce tastes and flavours from other cultures.

Smell

Smell and taste are strongly related. Most of us have experienced the inability to taste anything when suffering from a heavy cold. Like tastes, we all have our favourite smells and those we really dislike. Ask children to talk about their favourite smell and why they like it. Can they identify some familiar smells? What does it remind them of?

Allow the children to explore smells such as vanilla (new word), lemon, mild vinegar, chocolate, mint. Be careful not to use things with too sharp a smell or powdery things which may irritate some children, especially those prone to asthma.

Play the 'Guess the smell' game. Use 35mm film canisters to contain the smells. Make a few small holes in the top, put in the substance and clip the lid firmly on. Put liquids on a small plug of cotton wool so that, even if tipped upside down, there can be no spillage. The children can then try and guess the smell and tell you when or where they usually smell it.

If you have the space you could perhaps have a small garden, or even a large tub of fragrant plants such as herbs.

Assessment

Play 'Heads, shoulders, knees and toes'. Can the children point successfully to eyes, ears, mouth? Can they tell you what these various body parts do?

Note the children who can identify objects in a feely bag or name some familiar smells.

Play sound recognition games and note how many sounds the children know.

ACTIVITY

Minibeasts

Minibeasts are fascinating. When you think that a tiny ant still has all the life support systems of an elephant, it is really awe-inspiring. We may have phobias about spiders or snails but we must try not to pass these on to the children in our care. Try and think of the wonder of such small creatures and the complexity of their life-styles.

Learning objectives

❑ To be aware of the variety of small creatures to be found in the local environment;

❑ To learn to respect small creatures.

Getting started

Even the most barren of outside play areas can usually produce a few minibeasts if you know where to look. Before taking the children out on safari it is best to have a quick reconnoitre just to make sure that they won't be disappointed. Look in the cracks between building and playground and around any tufts of grass or weed. Look under window ledges or coping stones on walls. If you have a tree a gentle shake of a lower branch may produce something. If you have some earth, try digging a small area. You can make a small wildlife habitat by placing a few old logs and a big stone in a quiet corner. You will collect woodlice and

Early Learning Goals

❑ Find out about, and identify some features of, living things, objects and events they observe.

❑ Look closely at similarities, differences, patterns and change.

slugs if nothing else. An upturned dustbin lid with a few stones will make a shallow pond or miniature bog garden that will attract other creatures. Set this up three or four weeks before you plan to use it but then leave it as a permanent resource.

Before you take the children out, talk about what you might find and, most importantly, how you will care for whatever it is. Many children will think that spiders are for stamping on and beetles for squashing, so teaching them that these, too, are living creatures and deserve respect is a priority.

Using equipment

At first children should be encouraged just to look for small creatures without making any attempt to catch them - they can be a bit heavy handed! Gradually, as their motor skills improve, they may be able to coax an insect into a small pot or even use a paint brush to lift it gently.

Magnifying pots are useful for looking closely at minibeasts. Choose those with firmly fitting lids that don't drop off and are comfortable for little hands to hold. You can get very small ones but I think they are too small. They are easily put down and lost. They have a very small area of magnification and if the creature runs round the edge of the pot, as they usually do, then they are virtually invisible. The pots will also take only the smallest insects. At the end of each session make sure that all creatures are returned whence they came and all pots are empty and washed out. It is sad to take out the

bug pots only to find one of last year's ladybirds dried up in the bottom.

Creatures attached to leaves or bigger things such as slugs or snails can be collected in white plastic trays, the sort used for cat litter. If you use white ones the minibeasts show up well. They are particularly useful if you ever go pond dipping.

Pond dipping

This can be great fun but obviously needs close supervision. Raised ponds lessen the danger of falling in to some extent and are good for dipping. Other ponds may have railings round, but you need to explore the area thoroughly before taking any children. Some of you may be lucky enough to have access to a school pond. Even if you don't want to dip into the pond it is worth just sitting by the water on a summer's day, looking at the dragonflies and pond skaters and other small creatures that visit. It is also a good opportunity to talk about the dangers of water and the need to take care.

Patterns and predictions

Children can begin to look for patterns. How are the legs arranged on a beetle? How many legs does it have? Do all insects have the same number of legs? Where does a ladybird hide its wings? Do all insects have wings? Do they all hide them?

Do they always find the same sort of creature in the same sort of place? Can they see where some creatures have been? Are there holes in leaves or other clues?

After some experience can they begin to predict what they might find in certain places, such as under a stone or the roots of a plant or by the water?

Taking care of minibeasts

Some minibeasts will survive indoors for a short while. Snails are great entertainers. Place a little damp compost in the bottom of a plastic fish tank together with a few large stones or small rocks. A jam-jar lid makes a simple water dish and a few leaves or vegetable peelings will provide food. Put only a little in each day and remove the old food to keep it clean and sweet. Do make sure that you have a cover on the tank since slugs and snails are good escape artists! A piece of old nylon net curtain held on by a giant elastic band works well. Don't be tempted to make do with a piece of card or paper since they will just eat their way through it.

Children will spend a long time watching the snails crawl up the side of the tank. You can see the ripple of the muscle as it moves along. If you look carefully you may be able to see its mouth scraping algae from the side.

What does a snail feel like as it crawls across your hand? Do all snails have the same colour shell? Are they all the same shape? Do they all twist the same way? Talk about spirals and make some from paper. Hang them as mobiles to twist in the breeze. Use sausage-shaped pieces of clay or dough to make shell shapes. Make a collection of other types of shells and compare them.

You can use a similar tank or vivarium for keeping spiders. Add a few twigs from which the spiders can suspend their webs. Woodlice will also survive for a while but none of them should be kept for more than a few days before returning them to the wild. Any caterpillars should always be collected together with the leaves on which they were found since many caterpillars eat only one kind of plant and it is important to feed them the right variety. It also helps as a reminder of where they came from when it is time to return them to their natural habitat. Some children may be allergic to the hairy caterpillars so it is best not to handle them.

There are butterfly farms that supply chrysalises of moths and butterflies to hatch in the classroom in a fairly short time span. A suitable cage can be made from a large box. Cut most of each side out like a large window leaving the edges to make a frame around which you can stretch fine black net. Feeding instructions usually come with the moths or butterflies. Indian Moon moths are spectacular since they grow quite big. Do be aware that many moths and butterflies only live for a short time and success can be tricky.

Books

Wings, Stings and Wriggly Things; Disguises and Surprises Martin Jenkins, Big Sparks series (Walker).

Billy's Beetle Mick Inkpen (Hodder and Stoughton).

Stories

The Very Hungry Caterpillar; The Slug; The Very Angry Ladybird; The Very Quiet Cricket; The Very Busy Spider Eric Carle (Hamish Hamilton).

Songs

'Five Yellow Butterflies' in Play-along Songs (Hamish Hamilton).

'Little Arabella Miller' in This Little Puffin.

'The Ants Go Marching' in Okki-tokki-unga (A & C Black).

Poems

'Incy Wincy Spider'

'Slugs' John Kirching A First Poetry Book.

Butterfly larvae

Insect Lore, Suite six, Linford Forum, Linford Wood, Milton Keynes MK14 6LY.

Assessment

Watch children carefully as they observe small creatures. How careful are they? Have attitudes toward worms or spiders changed?

Make models or drawings of minibeasts and discuss how many legs you are going to put on. Some children will be able to tell you exactly how many legs a spider or an ant should have, while others will just say 'lots'.

Look at children's drawings of snails or slugs. How detailed are they? What particular observations have they made?

Observe how children use a magnifier. Are they able to tell you more about what they are looking at? Are they extending their vocabulary?

Sand, rocks and soil

Sand, rocks and soils are a readily available resource and great fun to explore. Sand is available from most educational suppliers. Many garden centres will let you browse round the edges of their rock piles for the smaller pieces if you explain what you want the rocks for. Monumental masons are also a good source although the choice there is often limited.

When sorting or exploring rocks, always work on the floor. That way, children are less likely to drop lumps on their toes. A rug under the samples will stop damage to polished floors. Avoid the very small samples of rocks you sometimes get, often stuck to a piece of card. They may look pretty but they do not give any idea of the weight or feel of rock.

If you try breaking any rocks children must be provided with eye protection.

Have some rubber gloves available for working with soil. Most children will be up to date with their tetanus jabs but cover any cuts before handling soil.

You can sterilise the soil by putting it in the microwave for a few minutes but this will kill off any small creatures in it and may not be popular with the cooks!

Learning objectives

❏ To look for similarities and differences;

❏ To observe changes in familiar materials;

❏ To think about what happened a long time ago.

Early Learning Goals

❏ Investigate objects and materials by using all of their senses as appropriate.

❏ Find out about, and identify some features of, living things, objects and events they observe.

❏ Look closely at similarities, differences, patterns and change.

❏ Ask questions about why things happen and how things work.

Sand

Many children will happily play in the sand tray all day if allowed to or, at least, until most of it is on the floor and there isn't enough left in the tray to do anything with! They can learn so much from playing with sand that a sand tray is really a must for every early years setting. If you don't have the space for the traditional tray on legs, then use a baby bath. Don't be tempted to use builders' sand. It is cheaper but much coarser and sticky. It also tends to stain everything bright orange. Washed silver sand can usually be obtained quite easily from most educational suppliers.

It is important that play in the sand is structured for at least part of the time. Think carefully about what it is that you want the children to learn from the sand and provide only the toys and equipment that will help to achieve those objectives. Too much apparatus at any one time just leads to chaos and confusion - and sand all over the floor. To get the best from the activity also means planning for a member of staff to

---

be with the group for at least some of the time. The adult can focus the children's thinking by asking the appropriate questions.

Encourage the children to feel the sand and let it run through their fingers. What is it made of? Use a magnifier to look at the separate pieces. Are they all the same? How are they different? If you have access to a simple binocular microscope (borrow one from the local primary school) some children may, at a later stage, be able to see that the sand is made up of tiny fragments of rock; sometimes you can even find little shells.

Wet and dry

Compare wet sand and dry sand. Many children are unlikely to remember what the sand was like yesterday and how it behaved compared with that in the tray today so you need to have both types available at the same time. Two large washing-up bowls, two baby baths or even two plastic storage trays will suffice. Make sure there are similar amounts of sand in each tray. Provide similar equipment in each tray, such as small buckets or plastic plant pots, small spades or large spoons, small plastic moulds, and so on. A small waterwheel is fun or a plastic funnel. If you don't have these then fold some stiff card to make a chute. If possible let the children help in making one lot of sand damp so that they can see it is just water that makes the difference.

Have two children playing with the damp sand and two with the dry. (You could have more or less depending on the size of the trays.) Ask them all to let the sand run through their fingers. What do they notice? What is the difference? Can they all pour the sand out to make a pile? Can they all make a sand pie? Who can run sand through the water wheel and make it turn? Who can fill the bucket through the funnel? Who can make shapes with the moulds? What happens if you make the sand very wet? Let children change places and investigate the differences for themselves.

After each of these activities the important question is 'Why?' and 'Why do you think that?' At this stage we are not looking for scientifically accurate answers but for children to have the confidence to express their ideas about how and why things happen. Most children will be able to tell you that they think the water 'sticks the bits together' but they may not have thought about it without being asked the question. Some of their answers show a great deal of thought and logic and provide opportunities to assess their understanding.

Soil

Soil is readily available and what better activity than making mud pies? Get the magnifiers out again and look for the similarities and differences between a dish of soil and a dish of sand. Depending on your soil the two samples may be different in colour. The soil may have bigger lumps and some pebbles. There may be 'long, thin bits' (dead plant material). If you have difficulty getting a soil sample, use some compost. A growbag is inexpensive and is good for growing your plants as well as for exploration. Make sure that children always wash their hands thoroughly after handling soil.

Investigate which is the best for making castles, sand or soil. Why? You may get a variety of opinions but encourage the children to listen to each other. In many investigations, different children or groups of children will have different

answers depending on how they set up the investigation. It is important that children begin to appreciate as soon as possible that there may be different answers to some questions but they are not wrong. Many children come into pre-school already conditioned that answers are either right or wrong and become worried about talking about their ideas or making a prediction, in case they are wrong. Help children to see that this is all part of the fun. It would be boring if everything always turned out just as we expected. What would be the point of investigating?

Collect different soils. Persuade colleagues or parents to bring a carrier bag of soil back when visiting friends or relatives in different parts of the country. The colour range can be dramatic. Keep your samples in plastic ice-cream tubs to stop them drying out too much. You can then use these as paints and paint cavemen pictures. The results make a good backdrop to a display of rocks and fossils.

Fossils

Fossils fascinate most children. They are fun to collect and sort into their different types, they are exciting to handle - and they are so old - even older than the teacher! (I was once asked if I played with dinosaurs when I was little!) Some types of gravel contain small fossils and it can be fun to sort through a trayful to see how many you can find. Try cutting out spiral shapes such as ammonites or pressing the shapes into playdough to make a pattern. Use a shortbread mixture to make fossil biscuits for snack time. At a later stage children could make their own fossil by pressing a fossil or other shape into some Plasticine and then filling the mould with plaster of Paris. Put a paper-clip into the back of the plaster before it dries to make a hook. When dry, take it from the mould and paint it or rub with a little shoe polish for a more natural effect. The plaster is brittle and hanging them up to display them saves tears (and mess).

Poems

'The muddiness of mud' Jack Prelutsky *Walker Book of Poetry*.

'We built a castle near the rocks' John Walsh Anglund *Read aloud Rhymes* (Walker Books).

'Mud Polly' Chase Boyden *Walker Book of Poetry*.

Rocks

Children at this stage do not have to know the names or origins of different types of rock but a few good samples make excellent talking points. There are specialist rock suppliers but a local monumental mason will often let you have off-cuts. These are good because you usually get polished and unpolished sides on the same piece, giving different textures. You may get rocks such as granite, slate or marble from this source. Other useful ones to add would be chalk, coal and sandstone. Make sure that the pieces are at least hand-sized so that children can feel the weight of the stone and perhaps see layers or different colours.

Again, look for similarities and differences. All are hard but the chalk and perhaps the coal leave dust on your hands. Why do some rocks have stripes or layers? Why do some have spots of different colours? You can see the spots even better when it has been polished. I wonder why? What do we use these rocks for? Where have they seen them? Many children these days have never seen an open fire so they may need to ask relatives or neighbours about the coalman coming.

Assessment

Most children should recognise sand and soil. Some will be able to tell you how they differ.

Given a tray of gravel, most children will be able to sort according to shape or colour but some children will be able to sort out any fossils.

Investigating sound

I approach a topic on sound with mixed feelings - the children usually love it but where can you put the group who are exploring the percussion instruments? (apart from the far end of the playground!). You may have some children who shout all the time or do not respond to some of the sounds or games you offer. It is worth asking parents or carers to have the child's hearing checked since it is not uncommon for young children to suffer some temporary hearing loss.

Learning objectives

❏ To identify some familiar sounds;

❏ To realise the importance of listening;

❏ To distinguish between loud and quiet sounds;

❏ To have fun making sounds.

Early Learning Goals

❏ Investigate objects and materials by using all of their senses as appropriate.

❏ Find out about, and identify some features of, living things, objects and events they observe.

❏ Look closely at similarities, differences, patterns and change.

❏ Ask questions about why things happen and how things work.

❏ Find out about and identify the uses of technology in their everyday lives and use information and communication technology and programmable toys to support their learning.

Listening walk

Go outside and listen to all the sounds in the environment. Can you identify them all? Which ones are natural sounds? (the wind, birds singing, dogs barking) Which are made by machines? (drills, radios, aeroplanes) When you get back, can you remember the order in which you heard the sounds?

What kind of sound can you make? We can use our voices to talk, sing, laugh, shout and cry. Can you whistle or click your fingers? Can you stamp your feet or clap your hands? Make sounds by gently slapping your leg or tapping your tummy.

Children should know that we use our ears to hear. How are they different from other animals' ears? Why can some animals move their ears? Can you still hear if you cover your ears? Can you tell which direction the sound is coming from? How do you know that sound is a long way away?

Loud and quiet

We often talk about sounds being loud or soft. Soft is one of those words that has several meanings so make sure the children know that in this context soft means quiet. Think of times when sounds need to be quiet: when baby is asleep, when we want to creep up on someone to give them a surprise (play games such as 'What's the time Mr Wolf?'), when we are listening to a story. Some children may be able to identify the difference between high and low sounds but it is quite difficult - it will come with practice.

Warnings!

When do we need sounds to be loud? Sounds are often used as warning signals. Fire engines, ambulances and police cars have warning bells or sirens to warn us of their approach. Cars have hooters and bicycles may have bells. What other warning sounds (car alarms, burglar alarms, sirens) might we hear?

Which sounds do we like to hear? Which don't we like? Which sounds tell us something? Why should we listen as well as look before crossing the road?

Some sounds send messages - alarm clocks, the telephone or pager, the ping of the microwave, church bells, the muezzin. Can they think of any other sounds that give you a message?

Name that sound

There are some good sound identification tapes available. You can, of course, make your own but in my experience it is far from easy. Unless you are an expert, splash out and buy one (or borrow one from your local library).

You might want to play the game of guessing the sounds all together at first so that any unusual sounds can be discussed. Children can then play in smaller groups. Some commercial tapes come with picture boards so that children can match the sound to the picture or play sound lotto. If you have headphones then you can set up a little listening corner.

Making music

Most instruments are played either by banging, plucking, scraping or blowing.

Use a short clip from a video of an orchestra to see how some of the instruments are played or you may know people who would be willing to come in and give a demonstration. Contact your local primary school and invite some recorder players, or any other instrumentalists, to come and give a short concert.

Cut pictures from a musical instrument catalogue to make a set of matching and sorting cards. Use pictures of a few familiar, simple instruments for the younger children but increase the number and type for older or more able children. Sort into sets according to the way in which they are played.

Percussion

Gather a collection of percussion instruments as funds allow. Meanwhile make the most of kitchen utensils or let the children make a few simple ones for themselves.

Saucepans and wooden spoons make excellent drums. Use a metal spoon for a different sound or bang on a breadboard. Use a bucket for a big drum. Do you get different sounds from the bottom or the sides? Two spoons banged together give yet another different sound. Experiment with different-sized spoons.

Hang a collection of utensils from a clothes line to make a set of tubular bells. Clay plant pots are good for this but they will break if hit too hard. Use four or five pots of different sizes. Hang them from a broom handle between two supports using a wooden bead threaded on a lace through the bottom of the pot. A padded drumstick gives a pleasant sound and is safer.

You can make rhythm sticks from pieces of dowel or broom handles. Saw them into suitable lengths and rub them with sandpaper to make sure there are no rough edges. The children will enjoy doing this for you. A coat of clear varnish gives them a professional finish.

Shakers

One of the easiest instruments for the children to make for themselves is the shaker. Find small pots with lids and you don't have the tricky job of covering the top. Experiment with different fillings. Try wooden beads, rice, lentils, pieces of lightly screwed-up foil, cotton wool, nuts and bolts, paper-clips and corks. Use your judgement about things that are safe to use according to the age of the child. Beware of seeds as many are poisonous. Which make the best sounds? Is the best sound the loudest sound? Which is your favourite?

Younger children will be happy to choose the filling they think looks best. Others may wish to try several before deciding the one they want. Have some spare pots so that they can compare the sounds before deciding finally. Fix the lid with a little sticky tape to prevent lentils shooting in all directions and encourage the children to decorate their shakers with any suitable materials.

Test different fillings and discuss them, then play each shaker behind a screen and see if the children can identify the filling.

Does it matter how much filling we put in the shaker? Put one wooden bead in a pot and shake. What sort of sound does it make? Put four or five beads in another similar pot. What do they sound like? Use a third pot and fill it with beads. Ask the children to predict what sort of noise that pot will make. The second pot will make a louder sound than the first. Many children will predict that the full pot will make an even louder sound because there are more beads. In fact the sound is muted because the beads have less room to move around. Older children may be able to explain this in their own way.

Twang!

Another simple instrument children have fun with is the elastic band guitar.

You need a small but fairly strong box. Empty tissue boxes are often used but they tend to collapse fairly quickly in the hands of an enthusiast. You also need a variety of elastic bands that are long enough to go tightly round the box. If you use bands of different thickness then you can get a wider range of notes. A small piece of wood under the bands acts like the bridge on a violin and by moving it along the box you can alter the pitch of the note. Take care that children pluck gently and don't pull the bands hard enough to snap them. Avoid narrow bands unless the children are being closely supervised.

You may want to work as a whole group when performing but it is useful to have a small corner where children can investigate sounds for themselves. If this is not possible, limit the exploration to a short time each day, for everybody's sanity, but make sure that each child gets a turn.

Save it

Some children may be able to play a simple tune on the flower pot bells or some chime bars if you have them. Encourage them to save their music to share with others. Some may be able to operate a simple tape recorder. Put different coloured spots on the necessary buttons and children will soon get the hang of it.

Assessment

Most children will be able to identify a number of familiar sounds. Look out for the children who don't seem to identify any - they may need a hearing check.

Most children will be able to distinguish between loud and quiet sounds and some may know the difference between high and low.

Can children sort pictures of musical instruments according to how they are played?

Amazing animals

Few people can resist a small furry animal and there is no doubt that a guinea pig, rabbit or other small creature can offer many learning opportunities for young children. Helping with the daily routine of cleaning and feeding can help them appreciate that all animals need care and that, like us, they need food, water and somewhere to live. But beware! If you are not fully committed to keeping an animal, don't. If looking after it becomes a chore then you could be giving out all the wrong messages about caring. In this case, it is much better to borrow an animal for a short time, enjoy caring for it, learn from it, and deliver it safely back to its owner before the novelty has worn off.

Learning objectives

❑ To appreciate the variety of animal life;

❑ To know that there are similarities between humans and other animals;

❑ To know that we need to respect and care for other living things.

Keeping pets

There are some animals and birds that you should avoid having in the nursery. (The Association for Science Education publishes a useful book, *Be Safe*, that gives all the dos and don'ts of keeping animals and plants.) Any animal should be bought from a reputable dealer so try to avoid the well meaning gift of someone else's out-grown rabbit!

Early Learning Goals

❑ Find out about, and identify some features of, living things, objects and events they observe.

❑ Look closely at similarities, differences, pattern and change.

Always make sure that children wash their hands after handling any animal or minibeast and be aware that some may be allergic to animal fur. Some children will spend ages grooming a co-operative guinea pig or rabbit but be sensitive to those who may be wary. They usually come round after a while. Encourage the children to take an active part in feeding, watering and cleaning out. Older or more able children may be able to keep records of the animal's growth, measuring and weighing it at regular intervals and filling in a simple chart.

As well as food and shelter, what else do the animals need? Why do we give hamsters and gerbils wheels in their cages for them to play on? Why do we provide them with things to chew and gnaw? Knowing that animals need food, water and exercise may help children to realise that humans are also animals and have the same basic needs.

Most young children will not appreciate that humans, too, are animals. Encourage them to look for similarities and differences between other animals and ourselves. They are usually quite good at noticing differences but may need help in identifying similarities.

All animals need to eat, but do we eat the same things? If you have a supermarket nearby, go and see how many different animal foods are on sale there. Set one group to count the variety of cat foods and another the dog foods. What other animals can you buy special food for?

What does your pet eat?

Make a pictogram of cat or dog food labels to find out which is the most popular pet food for the children's pets. Use the finished graph to practise and extend children's mathematical skills such as counting and consolidating language such as 'more than', 'less than', 'fewer', and so on.

Why not change the home corner into a pet shop for a while?

Do all animals drink?

What do they drink? How do they drink? Watch a cat lapping up milk or the guinea pig sucking at its water bottle. Can you find out how an elephant drinks? There are lots of videos of wildlife available but be selective about what you watch. You don't have to watch the whole thing - just a few minutes may be enough. Some videos have excellent photography but unsuitable commentaries for this age. Don't be afraid to turn the sound down and do your own.

Naming animals

Look at picture books and videos or CD ROMs and talk about the variety of animals there are. The children can perhaps name some of the animals and may even know where they come from. At a later stage use a big map of the world and pin pictures of a few favourite animals on the appropriate country or stick them on a globe with Blu-tack. A visit to a responsible zoo can help children to realise the size of the animals. In a book an elephant may look no bigger than the mouse on the next page.

If you have a co-operative pet shop in your area, they may be willing to bring more exotic animals in for the children to see. What does a snake really feel like? What does it eat? Why does a chameleon change colour? Why does the lizard have a long tongue? Why are some animals hairy and others smooth?

Hairy or smooth?

Encourage the children to use a magnifier to look at their arms and legs to see all the hairs there. If you have animals such as rats, mice or gerbils, children may notice that their babies

Assessment
Use a set of model animals or pictures and ask the children to name the ones they know. Most will be able to do this. Some will be able to tell you where they usually live.
Children should understand that baby animals grow into adult animals.

don't have fur when they are born. How does the mother look after them? How is it different from how human mothers look after their babies? Do all babies look like the adults? Can they match mums and babies?

A good set of model animals can prove an excellent investment. They can be sorted according to where they live, for example land, water, or sometimes, both, those that have fur and those that don't, those that live on the farm, those we might find in the zoo. Some children may be able to choose their own criteria and show themselves to be surprisingly knowledgeable. On one occasion I was baffled by the criterion used by a child until he patiently explained to me that one set contained herbivores and the other carnivores - and that was a three-year-old!

Bird watching

If you have space, a bird table or small bird bath can attract many feathered visitors. It needn't be elaborate - an old dustbin lid turned upside down works well. If it is a rubber one you may be able to remove the handle to make it more stable, otherwise sink the handle in the ground or support the lid with a few large stones. Put some large pebbles round the inside of the lid, leaving space for a small pond in the centre. This will make it easier for the smaller birds to reach the water and more difficult for children to fall in!

Stories
The Little Red Hen (Ladybird).
Rosie's Walk Pat Hutchins (Picture Puffin).
Noah's Ark and *Norah's Ark* Ann and Reg Cartwright (Picture Puffin).
Billy's Beetle Mick Inkpen (Hodder and Stoughton).

Rhymes
'Mum won't let me keep a rabbit' Brian Patten; 'Haiku' Roger McGough; 'Today I saw a little worm' Spike Milligan; all in *Puffin Book of Utterly Brilliant Verse* edited by Brian Patten.
Animal Poems compiled by Jennifer Curry (Hippo).
'An elephant goes like this, like that' and other animal rhymes and songs in *This Little Puffin* compiled by Elizabeth Matterson.

What do tadpoles grow into?

Watching tadpoles gradually turn into frogs never ceases to fascinate. You may take frogspawn from a garden pond but it is illegal to buy it, sell it or take it from the wild. Keep it in a shallow tank in a cool spot and out of direct sunlight. Put a rock in the water so that the developing frogs can crawl out. A little pond weed or watercress will provide food for the tadpoles but, as they start to develop their legs, give them a little fish food to provide the extra protein they need. You may need a cover for the tank at this point to stop the young frogs escaping. Make sure that the frogs are returned to a suitable place as soon as they are ready.

Keep a picture diary of what happens and how the tadpoles change.

Making puppets

Puppets and puppet making can be great fun and need not be at all complicated. Using puppets gives children the chance to act out their own or familiar stories and some children may become much more confident if they can 'hide' behind a puppet character. Even a very simple play means that children have to work together and co-operate.

Learning objectives

❑ To explore materials and simple techniques for making puppets;

❑ To explore shadows;

❑ To have fun.

Shadow puppets

Making shadow puppets fits in well with a topic on light and dark. It gives children further opportunities to explore shadows and how they are made. Use a torch and a screen or light-coloured wall and let the children play at making shadows with their hands. It is important that they realise that to make a shadow, their hands need to be between the light source and the screen. Simple shapes cut from card and stuck to thin garden canes or paper sticks can be used to make shadows on the wall and tell a story.

Of course, done this way, all the characters and workings are in front of the screen for all to see. Instead of making the shadows on a wall make a screen from light coloured material (preferably white) stretched over a frame. A basic one can be made by

Early Learning Goals

❑ Investigate objects and materials by using all of their senses as appropriate.

❑ Find out about, and identify some features of living things, objects and events they observe.

❑ Look closely at similarities, differences, patterns and change.

❑ Ask questions about why things happen and how things work.

❑ Build and construct with a wide range of objects, selecting appropriate resources, and adapting their work where necessary.

❑ Select the tools and techniques they need to shape, assemble and join the materials they are using.

stretching the material over a large PE hoop and holding it with big bulldog clips. Use the stick puppets in the usual way but this time encourage some children to go and watch from the other side of the screen. They should then just see the characters and not the people working them. You will need a fairly powerful torch for best results or use an overhead projector or desk lamp.

The children will need lots of time to play and experiment to find out the best way of making their shadows so that their heads aren't in the way or you don't see their hands. Putting the screen on a table so that the children can kneel down and operate the

puppets above their heads is one way but allow the children time to work this out for themselves before offering any suggestions.

Stick puppets can be successful using simple shapes that the children can cut out for themselves. Stick the shape to a thin garden cane or paper stick using sticky tape. Older or more dextrous children could cut shapes from their puppets and cover these holes with coloured tissue or acetate. Sweet wrappers work well and give the puppets more colour and character. Think of a butterfly with coloured wings or a bird with a beady eye.

Use puppets to tell the story of how a caterpillar turns into the beautiful butterfly or how frogspawn (use a good black pen to draw eggs on clear acetate) turns into a tadpole and then a frog. Children will have to work together and remember the order in which they need to appear.

Finger puppets

Finger puppets are by their nature quite small and some children may need quite a lot of help to make the basic shape. Felt is a good medium for more durable puppets but thin card is sufficient for short-term projects. You may have some old gloves from which you can cut the fingers. Encourage the children to use felt, card, felt-pen, wool sequins, and so on, to decorate the finger puppets and make them into different characters. They may choose to make characters to act out a familiar story or they may make the character and think of the story later.

Glove puppets

Make a simple glove puppet from a paper bag. These are easy for the children to get their hands in and to decorate but not too robust! However, with a little care, they will usually last as long as the children's interest. Offer a selection of different coloured bags from which the children can choose then decorate with paint, crayons or felt-pens. Alternatively they might want to cut features from other materials and stick them on to their bags to make other creatures. Cotton or small elastic bands wrapped tightly round the corners of the bag can make ears for an animal character.

More durable glove puppets can be made from old socks (well washed, of course!). Choose a colour to fit the character and decide what features are needed. Socks are much more flexible than paper bags and allow the children to add more character in the movement as well as the decoration. Tuck the sock down between fingers and thumb to give the character a mouth that moves. Encourage the children to look in a mirror to see how they move their mouths. Can they copy the movements with their puppets? Do all animals move their mouths in the same way? Are they the same shape? Look at pictures of animals and compare the shapes of their mouths or other features. You can buy 'googly' eyes quite cheaply and these are great fun to add character to a face.

Long socks that go up to the elbow make great snakes, slugs or caterpillars. Where are their mouths? What sort of pattern do they have on their skins?

Where are their eyes? How do they move? Questions such as these encourage children to look closely and help to develop observation skills.

Jointed figures

Cut body and limb shapes from card. Punch holes in appropriate places and fix together with paper fasteners.

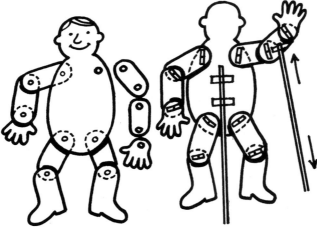

These puppets can then be stuck to a thin garden cane or paper stick and used as stick or shadow puppets. Some children might be able to attach another stick to either an arm or a leg to give more control over the movements of their puppet. They can then hold the body stick still but make the puppet kick a ball or wave by moving the other stick up and down. Some children will be happy with a figure that just has shoulder and hip joints while others may be able to cope with knees and elbows as well. Again encourage children to observe how the different joints work. Can they bend their knees or elbows backwards? How would we move if we didn't have joints? Practise in movement sessions. Most children will have encountered someone with a limb in plaster. How does that restrict movement?

String puppets need not be too complicated but children will probably need quite a lot of help to make them. Stuff an old sock or pop-sock with something suitable. Sawdust gives the puppet a little weight and makes it easier to control. Use a piece of thick string to tie round the sock to make a head. The string needs to be long enough to make the arms. Knot a bead at each elbow and at the ends of the string for hands. Tie a similar piece of string round the bottom of the sock for legs. Use beads for knees and feet. The puppets work better if the beads you use for hands and feet are quite heavy. Punch two holes 3-4 cm apart at each end of a strip of thick card, or better still, drill holes in a thin strip of wood. Attach thin string to each elbow and each knee. These strings should be long enough to reach from the relaxed limb, give some clearance over the head of the puppet and thread through the card strip. Finish off with a small bead to hold the string in place. Thread the arm strings through the inside holes and the leg strings through those nearest the end of the card strip. This helps to stop the strings tangling.

Experiment with different creatures. A scarecrow is suitably floppy while a caterpillar made from big beads works well.

Electricity

What would our world be like if there were no electricity? Think of the things we take for granted - lights, washing machines, mixers, radios, traffic lights, cookers - and a whole lot more. Even very young children are masters of the remote control or video game. But what is the basis of all these things?

Learning objectives

❏ To know that some things need electricity in order for them to work;

❏ To know that batteries can provide electricity for some devices;

❏ To know that some devices need mains electricity in order to work and that this source can be dangerous.

To work, any electrical device must have a complete circuit. Complicated devices have many complex circuits and investigating these is best left to the qualified electrician but simple circuits can be great fun.

Safety

Children should be taught never to investigate or play with any equipment that uses mains electricity. They should be warned of the dangers of playing near or climbing on electric pylons or electricity sub-stations, which are extremely dangerous. However, working with low-energy batteries is quite safe - and exciting!

Use an old catalogue and find pictures of things that use batteries and things that need mains electricity. Some things such as radios may work

Early Learning Goals

❏ Investigate objects and materials by using all of their senses as appropriate.

❏ Find out about, and identify some features of, living things, objects and events they observe.

❏ Ask questions about why things happen and how things work.

on either. Do they sound different if you use batteries rather than mains? What do you have in your building that uses electricity? Which sort is it?

Equipment

You will need a small amount of basic kit but once purchased this should last quite a while apart from replacing the batteries and the odd bulb. Younger children should not be expected to work with bare wire connections – it is far too fiddly. So you will need to provide wires or leads that are easy to connect.

Crocodile clips are a fairly standard form of connector but some children find these difficult to manage. Mount bulb holders on to a small block of wood (see diagram) and use curtain eyes to make bigger terminals for easier connection.

You can get bulb holders that have a connection into which you push a 4mm plug. These can be less frustrating for younger children or those who are less dextrous. You can buy leads with 4mm plugs attached. There are various kits available but these can be expensive. One, originally developed for children with special needs, has magnetic connections, which are easy to make.

For a simple basic kit you will need:

a battery, three leads (wires) with crocodile clips, a small bulb, a bulb holder mounted on a piece of wood with screw eye terminals and a small switch. Instead of buying a switch, you can make a simple one from two drawing pins and three paper clips on a small block of wood. This has the advantage of allowing children to see exactly how the connection is made.

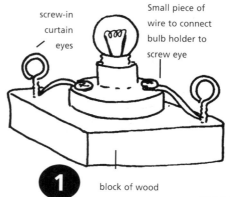

screw-in curtain eyes

Small piece of wire to connect bulb holder to screw eye

block of wood

1. Bulb holder
2. 4mm push in plug
3. Crocodile clip end to lead
4. Commercial type of switch
5. Paper clip switch

Batteries

The best types of batteries to use are either the 6-volt power packs or the smaller 4.5-volt flat type of battery with the metal strip connections. If you use ordinary round cells or batteries you will need to put them in a suitable battery box that has snap-on connections (rather like large press-studs) in order to make a good connection.

Do not buy too many batteries at once. They will gradually discharge over time so it is much better to buy them as you need them. I find the 6-v lantern batteries to be the most economical. They are much easier to store, they hold their charge well and they seem easier for the children to use.

Remember, the bulbs you use should be the same voltage as the battery. If you use a smaller voltage bulb it will shine brightly for an instant and then burn out. Never use anything bigger than 6v and avoid rechargeable batteries for this type of activity. They are fine for putting in toys that have special battery compartments but never use them where there is a possibility of children making a short circuit. A freshly-charged rechargeable cell can discharge all its energy in one spurt and become very hot.

Torches

Children find torches fascinating, so start off by looking at a selection of different torches. What do you have to do to make them work? What do you think happens when you operate the switch? You can get a good torch that has a see-through case that allows you to see exactly how it works when you press the switch.

Help the children to make a simple circuit from the bulbs, switch and wires so that they can press the switch and turn the light on and off. Compare it with the torch being switched on and off.

Next make the circuit without the switch but leave one of the battery connections undone. Can the children complete the circuit to make the bulb light? If you are feeling very brave, you could replace the bulb with a buzzer!

The children can use their new-found knowledge to enhance their models or pictures. Colour a bulb with red paint or felt-pen and poke it through a hole to give Rudolph or a robot a red nose. Put a light in your shoebox house or a flashing light on that fabulous machine for making lollipops. Flashing bulbs cost no more than the standard ones and can be great fun. Keep the model and circuit simple. You may need to provide some longer wires but avoid adding extra components.

3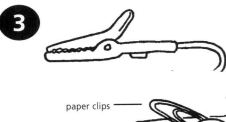

4

paper clips

drawing pins

block of wood

e connecton

5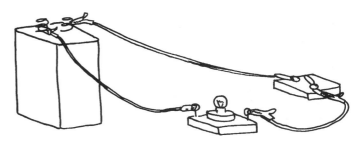

THEME

Seasons

Science all year round

Although it is not unknown to experience every type of weather in one day, we usually associate each season with a particular weather pattern. The weather has a great effect on our lives. It affects the type of house we live in and the clothes we wear. It dictates what type of animals and plants are to be found in the local environment. In some cases it affects the way we travel. It may even affect our mood.

Teaching children about the weather may take place as part of a project on the seasons but because it is so unpredictable it may be that you have to take the opportunity to explore any one type of weather as it occurs.

Learning objectives

❑ To know that there are four seasons;

❑ To know that we have different kinds of weather;

❑ To know that particular weather may be connected to a particular season;

❑ To appreciate that the weather has an effect on our lives;

❑ To be aware of seasonal changes in the environment.

Autumn

Autumn is a great season for collecting things: acorns, horse chestnuts and pine cones for sorting and weighing, crab apples and brambles for jams and jellies, and lots and lots of leaves. Now is the time, too, to plant bulbs ready for the spring. Hyacinths, crocuses or any of the miniature varieties of narcissus give good results in pots. Avoid the standard daffodils that tend to grow long and straggly indoors. Obviously, if you have a patch of garden then plant outside.

Leaves

Leaves are a readily available source of sorting material. As children learn to sort they are also beginning to classify objects. At first the differences they observe will be fairly gross but as they progress their observations should become more detailed. A very young child may sort 'leaves' from 'not leaves'. At the next stage, they might sort into piles of leaves of similar shape or colour. They might then begin to realise that although two leaves may be the same basic shape, they are not quite the same - one has a rough edge while the other is smooth, and so on.

Look carefully at a pile of leaves. Are they all the same shape? Can they sort them into sets? Make a record of the different leaves by doing rubbings or prints. Can they find the tree a particular leaf came from? How do they know which tree it is?

Leaves taken into the classroom soon disintegrate into a pile of dust. Choose three or four leaves of several different types and press them under a weight for a day or so, just to flatten them. Use one or two tiny spots of PVA glue to stick them on to separate pieces of card. Cover with clear, sticky backed plastic. You can then use these leaves

for matching or sorting games or for taking outside to 'find one the same as . . .'. They will last for several years if you use a reasonably stout card.

We often experience a windy spell in late autumn. It teases the remainder of the leaves from the trees and mounds them up along the pathways. Go for a walk and shuffle through the leaves. Think of all the words that describe the noise or the feel as you do. Are there any trees that still have their leaves? What do we call those sorts of trees? Older or more able children might explore how the leaves of evergreen trees and shrubs are different from the deciduous ones that have fallen. They are usually thicker, tougher and have a more waxy feel.

Getting ready for winter

As the season progresses, the weather turns cooler and we begin to get mists or even fog. A misty morning is a great time for looking at spiders' webs. The tiny drops of moisture make the finest webs into silver traceries. You may be lucky enough to see a spider hiding in the corner of its web waiting for an unwary fly. Look carefully under window ledges or in the cracks in a fence and you may find a chrysalis tucked away for the winter.

Which other animals get ready for winter? How do they do it? You may see flocks of birds gathering ready to migrate to warmer lands. Why are they leaving? Where are they going? Look on a globe to see how far some of them are going to fly.

Fog

Use a foggy morning to think about safety. Fog means that we can't see far so we need to listen extra hard. Car drivers can't see far ahead either, so there is a need for even greater care on the roads. Why do cars have their lights on in the fog? Why is it a good idea to wear something bright when walking along a road?

Wind

Most of you will agree that the wind has quite an effect on children's behaviour - the higher the wind the louder the noise! But how else do we know that the wind is blowing?

If you go outside you can feel the wind on your face. Perhaps it moves your skirt or your scarf. Look at the trees or the washing on the line. Can you see the clouds moving? Which way are they moving? Which way is the washing blowing? Can you see a weather vane? What does this tell us?

The children can make their own simple wind vanes by holding up strips of plastic or pieces of ribbon to blow in the wind. So that they don't let go and lose their ribbons, try tying the strips on to a large curtain ring or a cheap plastic bangle. This gives the children something to hold on to and gives sufficient weight to stop them blowing away if they are dropped. Use narrow strips cut from plastic carrier bags as streamers. Stand still and watch how the streamers move. Are they all blowing in the same direction? Do they blow that way all the time? Is it the same direction as the washing on the line? What does it tell us?

Older children could make a slightly

more sophisticated version that will indicate wind strength as well as direction. For this you need streamers of three or four different weights. Plastic carrier bags come in varying qualities and you need three or four ranging from the very thin to the more substantial. Cut narrow strips from each and tie them to a plastic bangle or a short piece of dowel. A pencil or paintbrush will do but it does mean that the wind measure has to be dismantled and can't be taken home for further investigation. You can use a mixture of ribbon, plastic, tape, and so on, providing they are different weights. Avoid using strips of paper as they soon tear and blow away.

When the device is held up in the wind the lighter strip should move in a fairly gentle breeze while a stronger wind is needed to move the heaviest strip. Take a reading every day to add to the weather chart. Use streamers of different colours to make recording easier. Older children should also begin to realise that their readings

should always be taken from the same place to make it fair.

Winter

In winter it gets colder. How much colder depends on where you live. The days are also shorter and this has an effect on how we live. Ask the children if they can remember what it was like in the summer. Was it light in the morning when they woke up? Was it still light when they went to bed? What sort of clothes did they wear? Did they play outside when they got home? Did they have the paddling pool out? What did the trees look like? Were there any flowers in the garden or park? How is it different now?

Don't try all these questions at once. Think about the focus of your session and ask the appropriate question. Younger children may find it difficult to remember what they had for breakfast let alone what it was like several months ago! Use pictures or holiday photographs to jog their memories.

Adopt a tree

If you have a tree nearby, try to take a close look at it each month throughout the year and watch how it changes. Take photographs, if possible, to help the children remember. Older children might do drawings or paintings to record the changes. You could collect

and press leaves from the tree, do some bark rubbings, measure how far round it is using a piece of string or ribbon. If it is a big tree, you could see how many children could join hands round it. Put all the information together to make a tree book, perhaps in a tree shape.

Birds

Children should also notice other

differences in the environment. Go out, if you can, and look for snails or beetles. Where have they all gone? What are the birds going to eat? There may still be berries that birds are feeding on and this could be a good time to reinforce the message about the danger of eating any berries they

find. A bird table can make a good talking point as well as helping children learn about caring. You do not necessarily have to have the traditional table, just a quiet spot where you regularly put out food or a peg from which you can hang a nut bag. The spot should be visible from a window so that the children can watch. Don't forget a small dish of water.

Encourage younger children to watch quietly and see what the birds do. Some children might begin to recognise one or two different types and match them to pictures in a simple identification book. Older or more able children could keep a record of the birds they see, perhaps on the computer, so that they can add to the list as they find new ones. They could investigate what the birds like to eat. Do they all like the same thing? Will they all eat at the same time? Can they all hang on to the nut bag?

What shall I wear?

Make a display of things we wear to keep us warm in the winter - coats, cardigans, jumpers, hats, scarves, mittens, woolly socks and warm boots. A favourite activity with my children was dressing Teddy for the appropriate weather. He had knitted jumpers, scarves, mittens and a woolly hat, shorts and T-shirt, a rain cape and even a pair of wellies.

Try a simple investigation to find out which types of clothes keep us warmest. Fill three hot-water bottles with reasonably hot water and 'dress' them in a) a tee shirt, b) a cardigan and c) an anorak or something similar. Let the children feel the bottles by putting their hands under the covering. Feel them again at regular intervals during the day and see which one stays warm longest. Older children could use a simple thermometer to measure the temperature. (Invicta makes some plastic strips that are calibrated as warmer than or cooler than 'me'.)

Snow and ice

You may have to use picture books or videos to give children an idea of what snow is like. If you are lucky enough to have a snowfall while the children are there then you will feel the excitement it brings with it. Dress up warmly and go out to investigate. Can they feel the flakes on their face? Can they catch them on their hand? What do they feel like? Is it harder to walk in the snow? Can they see where they have been? Can they tell their footprints from everyone else's?

You may only manage a short time outside before the children become too cold so it is worth talking about what you are going to be doing and looking for, before venturing forth, so that you can make the most of the time outside. Take several small plastic bags of snow in with you. Put them in different places or wrap them in different materials. Wait about 15 minutes and see what has happened to them.

Back in the warm and dry, think about what it would be like to live where it is really snowy. What sort of clothes would you need to wear? How would you travel or get to school? What sorts of animals live where it is very cold? What do they eat? Use your set of model animals to sort out all those that live in cold places.

While you may not get snow you will almost certainly get ice. What happens to flowers or leaves after a frost? Why has the puddle gone hard? Can you walk easily on an icy path? Can you see the patterns on the window? What happens if you breathe hard on the window? What are icicles made of? Put a little water in the freezer compartment of the fridge to make some ice cubes or, more fun, freeze some fruit juice. What are they like when they come out of the freezer? What happens to them if you leave them in a dish for a little while? Why have they changed? Could you change them back again?

Older children might investigate how long an ice cube will last. You will need several ice cubes, each in its own yogurt pot or saucer. Ask the children

where they think would be the best place to keep it - on the window ledge, in the fridge, by the radiator, in the cupboard, outside. Which one melts first? Which one lasts longest? Why?

You might want to do this activity during a spell of frosty or snowy weather when the children have experienced some icy conditions. Alternatively, it could be done in the summer and related to keeping your ice-lolly in one piece.

Spring

Spring is a magical time with new life bursting everywhere. Don't forget to go and look at your adopted tree because changes will be happening quite quickly now. What is happening to the bulbs you set in the autumn? How has the weather changed? Is it still dark when you get up in the morning?

Babies

Many animals produce their young in the spring to take advantage of the increased availability of food supplies and so that the offspring can build up their resources before the onset of winter. If you have a farm nearby this is a good time to visit and see the lambs. Some of the children may have baby brothers or sisters and they can help you compare how human babies are cared for compared with those of other animals. You may get some fairly down-to-earth comments about 'poo' and 'wee', but at this stage children are very interested in bodily functions and have not yet developed the inhibitions that make such things more difficult to discuss later. Treat any comments seriously and frankly and explain in words that the children understand.

At some farms you can see eggs hatching and the new chicks emerging. This never ceases to amaze and some of you may be able to borrow or hire an incubator from a local secondary school or science centre so that you

can hatch a few eggs of your own. There are a variety of incubators available but they do tend to be expensive. Perhaps it would be possible to join with another setting or school to buy one? Make sure that the source from which you get your fertile eggs will take the chicks back once they are hatched. Hatching chicks takes about 21 days. You do need to be committed but the rewards are worth it.

Rain

Spring can often be quite wet, after all 'April showers bring forth May flowers'. (Older children might enjoy finding other rhymes or sayings to do with the weather.) While we may not enjoy prolonged periods of rain, it is necessary for crops to grow. What would it be like if we had no rain at all? Are there places in the world where it never rains? What do we call those places? Does anything live there?

Picture books and videos can help to give children some idea of what deserts are like. Look at a cactus plant (not one of the very prickly ones) and talk about how they can store water in the fleshy stems. Put a plant like a Busy Lizzie and a cactus next to each other on a sunny window ledge. What happens? (The Busy Lizzie can quickly be revived by soaking it in water.)

Keeping dry

How do we keep dry in the rain? What special clothes do we wear? Do all materials keep the water out? Try testing different materials to see if they let water through. You need a selection of pieces of different materials such as woven and knitted fabric, lace curtain, net, plastic sheet, felt and paper. Let each child choose a piece of material to test. Place it over the top of a clear container and fix it with an elastic band. (Use the bottom half of a plastic bottle. Cut the bottle in half and you have a container and, if you turn the top upside down, a funnel that fits the container perfectly. Bind the edges with some plastic tape for safety.) To make it more fun I put a plastic Teddy in the bottom of the container before fixing the material on then we pour water on to the material and see if Teddy gets wet. It is a good idea to do this in the water trough, a big tray or even outside. It can get rather splashy.

Younger children will just have fun trying to make Teddy wet but older children should tell you why they have chosen a particular material. Some will say it is because they like the colour or feel of the material but some may begin to talk about the structure of the material. Guide them towards looking carefully to see if the material has lots of holes in it. It is a good idea to have a magnifier handy to see that even a closely woven fabric has small holes between the threads.

Puddles

If you have accessible puddles after it has rained, go out and draw a chalk line round the edge of one. Choose one that is not too deep. Then go out at regular intervals (say every hour), and draw another line round the puddle. Is the line in the same place? What is happening? Where is the water going? This obviously works best on a sunny day when the water will evaporate quite quickly.

Some children will say that it is soaking into the ground and to some extent this may be true, but most of the water will be evaporated. Try putting a shallow tray of water next to a puddle and see what happens. That water, too, should disappear but it can't have soaked into the ground this time. So where has it gone? Remember at this stage you are not looking for scientifically correct explanations but for the children's own ideas. They will give you an insight into how the child is thinking and help you to plan your next steps.

Younger children will just be happy to see that puddles disappear. You could have a competition to see which puddle lasts longest. Which one do they think will last longest? Why do they think that? You could show older children the steam coming from a kettle and ask where they think the steam is going. This may help them to start thinking about the concept of evaporation.

Summer

Summer is a time when, hopefully, we can play outside and enjoy the sunshine. Children should always be protected from sunburn and warned never to look directly at the sun, even through sunglasses.

Shadows

A nice sunny day is a good time to investigate shadows (for more activities, see page 55) and the better weather may provide more opportunities for going out and looking for plants and minibeasts in the environment. It is also a good time for doing really splashy things with water!

Water play

Empty washing-up bottles make ideal squirters. What do you need to do to make the water come out of the bottle? Who can squirt furthest? Can you hit a target?

Experiment with simple siphons and see if you can use one to empty a bucket or bowl. You need a piece of tubing between half a metre to a metre long and sufficiently narrow so that the children can cover the end with their finger or thumb. You will need to show them how to fill the pipe with water and cover the end as they take it out to make sure no air gets in.

Bubbles

Bubbles are a never-ending source of delight. They are best investigated outside since some children can be

sensitive to the tiny drops of bubble mixture in the air, particularly those who suffer from asthma. It is also a good idea to have a few disposable plastic gloves for children who have skin conditions. Some younger children may need to be shown how to blow bubbles if they have not done so before. (A 20 per cent solution of washing-up liquid makes a good bubble mixture.) You can also make bubble wands from pipe-cleaners but be careful of sharp ends. (A set of three sturdy bubble wands or blowers can be purchased quite reasonably from Trylon. A set comprises three shapes, triangular, square and circular, all properly finished with a solid plastic handle.)

Can you blow a different shape bubble? How many different colours can you see in the bubbles? What happens when the bubbles hit the floor? What happens if one lands on your coat or cardigan? What happens if you blow gently? What happens if you blow hard? Can you catch one? Can you pass it to a friend?

By the seaside

Not all children get to the seaside but it still holds a fascination for them. They will have heard about it and seen programmes on TV and know about sharks and giant octopus if nothing else.

Make a display of seashells. Invite the children to contribute. Look for all the different shapes and colours. What are shells? What might have lived in them? Compare them with snail shells. How are they the same? How are they different? Use a video of life under the sea to show the children that shells are actually parts of living creatures that move and feed.

It is worth having a collection of smaller shells for counting, sorting, matching and weighing. You can often get bags of interesting ones from hobby shops or garden centres. Make sure you sort out the really tiny ones before you give them to the children.

Add some shells to the sandpit. Can you press a shell into the sand to make a pattern? Does it work better with wet or dry sand?

Explore materials further by using plaster of Paris and watching how it changes from a powder, to a soft, thick liquid when you add it to water and then to a hard material as it sets.

Put a layer of damp sand, playdough or Plasticine in the bottom of a small plastic container such as a margarine or coleslaw tub. Press a shell into the dough to make a pattern. Smear a little grease round the sides of the pot. Put a small amount of water into a yogurt pot and add enough plaster of Paris to make a thick creamy paste. Pour the mixture gently into the mould and allow it to set. Feel the sides of the pot as it hardens. The chemical reactions within the plaster cause heat to be given off and this can be felt as the plaster sets. Before it sets completely press a paper-clip gently into the plaster to form a hook. When hard, turn the casts out. The resulting plaques can be painted or brushed with a little shoe polish for an antique effect. The hook allows them to be hung up to make a display rather than left on a table where they soon get rather the worse for wear.

Picnic time

Summertime is a good time for picnics even if it is only outside on the playground. What is a picnic? What do we need? Ask the children for their ideas. Start planning well ahead so that you can make lists, do the shopping, perhaps even have time to grow some cress for the sandwiches.

Having decided on the food that you are going to take, how will you get it there? How can you wrap food to keep it safe and fresh? Make a collection of different sorts of packaging - plastic boxes, plastic food bags, cling-film, paper bags, greaseproof paper. Which sort of packaging will be best for which type of food? Why?

Investigate cool bags or boxes and find out how long they keep cool. Put a few ice cubes in two small plastic bags. Put one in the cool bag and leave the other on the table or some convenient place. Which melts first? Talk about why we need to keep food cool and why we need to wash our hands before handling it.

How will you take the drinks? Why are plastic bottles better than glass ones? What should we do with the rubbish when we have finished? Why is it dangerous to leave plastic bags and glass bottles around? It is never too soon to encourage children to take care of and pride in their environment.

Assessment

As children fill in the weather chart you can assess their understanding of the different types of weather.

Note those children who bring offerings of unusual leaves or tell you of the spider or beetle they saw. They are obviously developing their observational skills.

Most children should know that we have different seasons. Some children will be able to name them. Younger children may not appreciate the cyclical nature of the seasons but older children should begin to appreciate that we have the same seasons each year and that our environment changes accordingly. Use some pictures of typical seasonal scenes or objects and ask the children to sort them into appropriate groups. Some children might be able to dress Teddy for a given season.

Suppliers

Trylon, Thrift Street, Wollaston, Northampton. Tel 01933 664275 Suppliers of primary science equipment including bubble blowers and long plastic prisms.

Incubators: Egg incubator for ten eggs (approx £140) from Philip Harris, Lynn Lane, Shenstone, Lichfield, Staffs WS14 0SS Tel: 01543 480077

Descriptive thermometers from TTS, Monk Road, Alfreton, Derby DE55 7RL Tel: 01773 830255

Stories

In the Rain with Baby Duck Amy Hest (Walker).

Mrs Mopple's Washing Line Anita Hewitt (Red Fox).

Elmer's Weather David McKee (Andersen Press).

The Wind Garden Angela McAllister and Clark Fletcher (Red Fox).

Camels Don't Ski Francesca Simon (Levinson Books).

The Snowman Raymond Briggs (Hamish Hamilton).

Tom and Pippo in the Snow; Out and About with Tom and Pippo Helen Oxenbury (Walker).

Poems

'I hear thunder'; 'This is how the snowflakes play about'; 'The autumn leaves have fallen down'; all from *This Little Puffin*.

'The Wind' R L Stevenson *The Child's Garden of Verse* (Puffin).

Traditional weather rhymes

'April showers'

'Rain, rain, go away'

'The North wind doth blow'

What can water do?

Children need lots of experience in order to develop their ideas about how water behaves. There are lots of water troughs or trays available, but children will have just as much fun and learn just as much if all you have is a large washing-up bowl or baby bath. The important thing is that children can try out their ideas and develop concepts about water.

Early Learning Goals

❑ Investigate objects and materials by using all of their senses as appropriate.

❑ Find out about, and identify some features of, living things, objects and events they observe.

❑ Look closely at similarities, differences, patterns and change.

❑ Ask questions about why things happen and how things work.

❑ Find out about and identify the uses of technology in their every day lives.

Water is wet. It can be hot or cold. It can be silent or noisy and it is essential to life. What else does water do?

❑ Water can flow outwards or downwards;

❑ Water can take the shape of its container;

❑ Water will go solid if it is made very cold;

❑ Water will turn into a gas if made very hot;

❑ Water makes things wet;

❑ Some things will dissolve in it.

Learning objectives

❑ To explore the properties of water;

❑ To understand the language such as full, empty, enough, too much;

❑ To know that animals and plants need water to sustain life.

Up and down

Don't be tempted to put all the toys in the water tray at the same time. Be selective. Think carefully about what you want the children to learn from the session and choose the equipment accordingly. If you want them to experience water flowing, provide funnels, jugs, plastic tubing and a watering can, so that they can pour water from and through things. What does it feel like as it flows over their hands? Can they catch it?

Does water always flow downwards? How far will it spread? Can you make it flow upwards? Encourage children to explore simple siphons or water pumps. How do they work? Can they empty the trough or bowl into a bucket using a piece of plastic pipe? You have to make sure that the pipe is full of water, put a finger or thumb over one end and insert this quickly into the bucket. Your siphon should work so long as the pipe remains full of water.

There are some simple see-through pumps that allow children to see the workings inside. Can they explain how it works to a friend? Small plastic pipettes are cheap and allow the children to practise fine motor control. Plastic syringes are useful. Some people have reservations about introducing them to children because of the obvious implications, but they are useful for measuring small quantities. Emphasise that they should never pick up a syringe that they find outside but also that syringes have good uses as well as bad.

Fill it up

Playing in the water tray is an ideal opportunity to introduce language such as full, empty, enough, too much, overflowing. For this you will need a selection of containers, jugs and plastic bottles. Do all the containers hold the same amount? How could you find out? How do you know when something is full?

Some children may be ready to consider what 'full' means? Let them investigate filling a small container with beads. Try and get a bowl deep enough to dunk the container under the beads in order to fill it. Is it easy to get the pot into the beads? Do you have to put beads in with your hands? Is the pot really full? What about the spaces between the beads? Do the same thing with dry sand using another container the same size and shape. How easy is that to fill? Are there still spaces around the grains of sand? Now try it with water. How easy is it to dunk that under water? Does anything come

out of the container as the water goes in? What is in the bubbles? Is the pot really full of water or is there still some air in it? Compare the three pots. Which pots could still hold more water? Where would the water go?

You are not looking for accurate scientific explanations at this stage, that will come later, but you need to encourage children to think and to have the confidence and language to talk about their ideas.

Changing shape

Children usually need little persuasion to empty the containers but what happens when they do? How does the water behave? What happens to water if you gently pour (spill) it on to a tray? Does it stay where you put it? Does it spread out? If you tip the tray, does the water flow up or down? What sort of shape is the water on the tray? How does it change its shape when you put it in something tall and thin? Have fun experimenting with odd-shaped bottles and jars. With clear plastic ones there is no danger of cuts from broken glass. (Empty bubble bath bottles are ideal.)

Mop it up

Which material mops up spills best? There are usually enough opportunities to put this into context! Provide a sponge, a synthetic kitchen cloth, a paper towel, a piece of plastic sheet and a dish cloth. Ask children to choose the material they think will hold the most water.

Test the materials by dunking them in a bucket of water. Squeeze them hard and let them go again so that they are thoroughly soaked. What do you notice when you squeeze each one under the water? Did you see bubbles from some?

When each material is thoroughly soaked, squeeze each one out into a separate tray and compare the yield. How hard did you have to squeeze to get all the water out? Did you really get it all out? At first children may just estimate the amounts of water - a little, a lot, more than, and so on. Pour the water into some kind of tall containers in order to make a more accurate comparison. A simple, quick and cheap measuring cylinder and funnel can be made from an empty plastic bottle. Bind the edges with thick sticky tape to cover any sharp bits. Adding a little food colouring to the water makes it easier to see and talk about, especially if you use a different colour for each material you are testing. Don't ask the children to compare more than two or three to begin with. Later they may compare more samples and begin to measure the amounts of water mopped up, at first with non-standard measures such as egg cups or yogurt pots, gradually moving to standard measures and recording their results in simple tables.

Drying time

Once you have lots of wet and soggy materials, investigate which of the materials dries the quickest. Dolls' clothes and Teddy's clothes provide a wide range of materials to investigate. Encourage the children to feel the materials and say which one they think will dry the quickest and why.

Water of life

Plants and animals both need water. Books and videos can give children some ideas about what it is like in a desert where there is little water and what happens in a flood when there is too much water. They know what it feels like when they are thirsty and need to drink.

Some plants and animals have adapted to live in water. How are fish different

from other creatures? How do they swim? What do they eat? Try keeping a goldfish for a while and learn to care for it. What else lives in water? Turn a corner of the room into an underwater scene with hanging seaweed made from tissue, jelly fish and fish mobiles.

Do a simple investigation to find out if plants can live without water. You will need two small pot plants. Put them in the same place in the room, water one regularly and don't give the other any water at all. Watch carefully what happens to each plant. Some plants, such as Busy Lizzie, wilt quickly if left in a sunny spot for an hour or two and are deprived of water. Give them water and they will recover just as quickly or put one flower in a jar of water and a second flower in an empty jar. Watch what happens. Which one dies first? Why? What happens if you use white flowers and put a little blue food colouring in the water? Why do you think the flower has turned blue?

Get children thinking and talking, to allow them to develop their ideas by trying to describe and explain what they see and building their confidence by valuing each contribution.

See also page 50, 'Puddles', for more ideas to do with water.

Assessment

Children should know the vocabulary 'full' and 'empty'. Some will begin to understand that water changes shape to match the shape of its container.

Assess children's ideas about floating and sinking by asking them to predict which things will float and which will sink and why they think that.

Talking about how to care for their pets or the plants in the setting will help you to find out if the children understand that all living things need water.

Colour

Through the rainbow

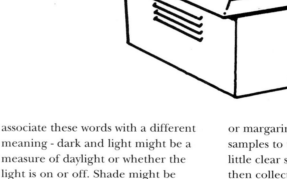

Rainbows are a constant delight and a source of awe and wonder. You may be lucky enough to see one during a session but the chances are that it appears just after the children have gone home. You can make your own with a jar of water on a sunny window ledge, but I have always found this method as unpredictable as waiting for the real thing! However, if you have access to an overhead projector and a prism, you can have a rainbow as often as you like. Just angle the prism on one of the edges over the projector and hey presto!

Learning objectives

❏ To recognise and name colours;

❏ To know that light comes from different sources;

❏ To know the difference between light and dark;

❏ To know that shiny things reflect light.

Shades of colour

Make colour displays choosing a different colour each week. Start off with a drape and some pictures and ask the children to contribute items of the appropriate colour or even come dressed in that colour for the day. Talk about how things that are the same colour are not all exactly the same - they may be darker or lighter, or a different shade. It is important to talk about these words and not just take it for granted that children understand what we mean. They may already associate these words with a different meaning - dark and light might be a measure of daylight or whether the light is on or off. Shade might be where we go to get out of the sun.

On safari

Children who know their colours well might go on a rainbow safari to see if they can match shades more exactly. You will need some small cards with blobs of colour on or some paint-mixing shade cards. Cut them up, give each child two or three shades and send them off to find something that matches as closely as possible. This is a particularly good activity if you have access to a field, wildlife area or other such space. Let the children work with a partner. Give each pair an ice-cream or margarine pot and stick the colour samples to the bottom of the pot with a little clear sticky tape. The children can then collect their finds and show them to you. You will need to do a little research to make sure that you give them colours that can be matched.

Children can explore colour in so many ways. Paintings, finger painting, chalks, crayons and felt-tips all help children work out their ideas about colour. Talk about these ideas. Which is their favourite and why? Which ones make them feel happy, sad, cold, hot? Can they use colours to make a pattern - stripy, spotty or even checked? What happens when two colours start to mix? Can we mix colours to make new ones?

What happens when you look through coloured acetate? Which colours change? How do they change? Cut a shape from the middle of two sheets of card. Fix a small sheet of coloured acetate between the two to make a coloured window. This makes it easier to handle and stops the acetate from getting quite so sticky.

> **Early Learning Goals**
>
> These activities will help you work towards all of the science and technology ELGs. They also cover elements of the geography and history related goals as well.

Can we see in the dark?

Most children have never experienced total darkness. Even when they are in bed the chances are that there is a night light, the light on the landing or a street light shining through the curtains. Sometimes, if you go on a visit to some caves or a mine the lights are switched off and, for a moment, you can experience complete darkness. You can make a dark den or 'cave' for the children to play in. You will need a very large cardboard box, such as packaging for a freezer. Make a flap for a door in one side. Fix some beads inside and out to make a handle so that the door can be pulled shut and paint the inside black. Provide a torch and a picture book. What can the children see when they go in the box? Can they read the book? What happens when they switch the torch on? Why can they see now? Some children may be reluctant to go in the box at first. Don't force them. When they hear the whoops and yells from the others, curiosity usually overcomes reticence.

If we need light to see, where does it come from? We don't have lights on in the daytime outside, so where is the light source? Most children will be able to tell you about the sun. It is important that children are taught never to look directly at the sun even through sunglasses or filters. If the sun provides light by day, where do we get light from when the sun isn't there? Some children may be able to tell you about the moon and the stars. In the winter, when the days are shorter, it is possible to see the waxing moon during the early morning as the children are arriving and the waning moon, later in the lunar month, as the children go home. The moon has no light of its own. It shines with the reflected light from the sun.

Make a collection of other light sources and talk about how they work. How did people see in the dark before we had electricity? What would it be like to have no street lights? Perhaps there is someone in the community who could come in and talk about what it was like in the blackout during the war when they were small. (For more ideas, see 'Electricity', pages 44-45.)

Shadows

On a nice, sunny day you can have lots of fun with shadows. If something gets in the way of the sunlight, a shadow forms. Where is your shadow? Is it in front or behind? Is it always in the same place? Is it always the same size? Can you catch your shadow and jump on it? Can you catch someone else's shadow? Can you draw a picture of you and your shadow?

Many young children will happily draw a picture of themselves and their shadow standing alongside as a totally separate entity. They need lots of experience and discussion to help them understand that their shadow is always attached to them and that it will move and change accordingly. Try experimenting with shadows inside using a torch or lamp and a screen.

Can you walk round the building keeping in the shadows all the way? Does it matter what time of day you try to do this? Stand in a special place and ask a friend to draw round your shadow. Go out again later in the day and stand in exactly the same spot. Where is your shadow now? Why do you think it has moved?

Transparent, translucent, opaque

Some materials are special - you can see through them. Others stop you seeing anything at all and some you can sort of see through, but everything is fuzzy. These are the sort of descriptions you may get from a child to describe transparent, translucent or opaque materials. Provide a collection of materials for the children to sort.

Stories

All the Colours of the Earth Sheila Hamanaka (Mantra).

A Dark, Dark Tale Ruth Brown (Andersen Press).

The Park in the Dark Martin Waddell and Barbara Firth (Walker Books).

Poems

'My Shadow' R L Stevenson *A Child's Garden of Verse* (Puffin).

Look around the setting or ask children to look at home and find out where materials with these particular properties are used. We can see through glass so it is useful for windows, but what about the glass in the bathroom window?

Why is it sometimes useful to have a window in a door? Why don't all doors have windows? Why do we sometimes keep things in clear plastic wallets? Younger children may be able to use the word 'transparent' but 'opaque' and 'translucent' will come later.

Assessment

Are children able to recognise different colours and name them?

Can they draw or paint a rainbow? Some might even get the colours in the right order.

Most children will know that on a sunny day they have a shadow. Some children will understand that when light is blocked a shadow is formed. How would they arrange the light and the object to make a shadow on a screen?

Children should know the difference between light and dark.

THEME

All about me

Who am I?

Any small child is, as far as they are concerned, the centre of the universe. Everything revolves about them and should be done to their bidding! Our job is to help them understand that, important though they are, they are only part of a much bigger scene. They need to become aware of their own bodies and what they are able to do with them. They need to begin to appreciate the similarities and differences between themselves, other human beings and other animals. Most young children will not appreciate that humans are animals and will need to have the similarities between species drawn to their attention. For example, all animals breathe, eat, excrete and reproduce.

A great deal of the work about 'Me' is also linked with Personal, Social and Emotional Development: learning to share and consider other people, learning to work together and listen to the ideas of others, knowing that we have different feelings and that we can affect the feelings of others, understanding that friends are important.

Learning objectives

❑ To be able to name external parts of the body;

❑ To encourage skills of observation;

❑ To identify similarities and differences between themselves and other children;

❑ To know the importance of dental hygiene;

❑ To begin to understand the importance of a healthy diet;

❑ To understand that babies grow into adults.

Who am I?

Most children will be able to tell you their name, and one of the first things we teach them is to recognise that name on coat pegs, shoe bags, drawers and so on. One effective way of helping them is to take a photograph of each child when they come in for their preliminary visit. Have them developed by one of the multi-print laboratories, so that you can use

Early Learning Goals

These activities will help you to work towards the following ELGs:

❑ Find out about and identify some features of, living things, objects and events they observe

❑ Look closely at similarities, differences, pattern and change

They are also good for Personal, Social and Emotional Development.

the bigger photograph on the child's coat peg and then stick the other two to spring-clip clothes pegs for the children to use to identify their work or to indicate that they have had their snack.

Most children coming into your setting will know where their arms and legs, hands and feet are. Most will be able to point to the features on their faces, though you may still have one or two who are not quite sure. Action songs such as 'Heads, shoulders, knees and toes', 'Put your finger on your nose, on your nose' or any of the many finger rhymes such as 'One finger, one thumb', or 'Tommy thumb' will help the children learn the names of parts of the body.

Rogues' gallery

Use plastic mirrors to help children recognise and name the features on their own faces. Children at an early stage will probably just paint fairly stylised, smiley faces. Playdough, collage, faces on paper plates can all help children learn more about their faces. Playdough is particularly useful since you can talk about different feelings and the children can change the faces they have made according to the feeling they are thinking about to show happy, sad or angry expressions. Software such as *Smart Alex* allows children to record likes and dislikes on the computer. Programs such as *Face Paint* allow them to experiment with changing features and expressions.

Self-portraits encourage the children to look carefully at their faces and encourage general observation skills.

❑ What colour hair do they have?

❑ Is it long or short?

❑ What colour eyes do they have?

❑ What shape are their eyebrows?

Even very young children can be surprisingly accurate in their observations while others will need encouragement to paint what they see rather than what they think they see. In a way, this is a subtle beginning to knowing the difference between fiction and reality. You obviously want to encourage children to be imaginative but they also need to understand that, sometimes, it is important to record what they see or do.

A long mirror will enable children to see themselves in their entirety. Try and get hold of an off-cut of silvered plastic. (You may have a found materials centre near; if not, you can sometimes get it from a firm specialising in shop displays.) We had great fun with a long piece that I fixed firmly to the wall at the top. You could lift it up until you had two heads and bodies but no legs or feet; bent the other way you were all legs and no head!

Same or different?

Encourage the children to look for all the things we have in common before looking for differences.

❑ We all have eyes - but how do they differ?

❑ We all have hair (or most of us do), but how is it different?

❑ Is everyone the same size?

❑ Who is the tallest?

❑ Who has the biggest feet? (Treat sensitively)

❑ Whose fingers are longest?

Very young children may just talk about the differences or move themselves into different sets according to the chosen criterion. Compare handprints and footprints against each other and then mount as peacocks, rainbows or in other imaginative ways. At a later stage children may make simple charts or pictograms, perhaps using a graphing program on the computer.

If you have children with special needs in your group, this is a time when you can help children to understand and accept the differences between them. We are all different, it is just that some people have bigger differences than others and some of these differences may mean that they need a little extra help in one way or another.

Keeping healthy

This aspect of work on 'ourselves' again has strong links with personal and social development. Children need to become independent in dealing with personal hygiene as soon as possible. Washing hands after using the toilet and always before handling food should become second nature but we all know how much reminding has to take place. Tell children the reason for all this cleanliness, that germs can pass from one person to another, particularly on food, but beware of over stressing it since some children become obsessed with everything being covered in 'nasty germs'.

Cooking activities provide lots of opportunities for good science and technology and give excellent opportunities for talking about and practising good hygiene routines (see pages 24-29).

Looking after your teeth

Looking after your teeth and keeping them healthy is something else that can't start too soon. It is worth contacting your local health authority to see if they have a dental team that will visit or have resources that you can borrow for a short time. Giant toothbrushes and enormous teeth can make the learning more fun and more memorable.

Use those plastic mirrors again to look at teeth.

❑ Are they clean and bright?

❑ How many teeth do you have?

❑ Are they all the same shape and size?

❑ Why do you think we have different kinds of teeth?

Having healthy teeth is also part of healthy eating. At first children may just learn about the need to keep their teeth clean but later they should begin to think about how what they eat can affect their teeth and their general health. Healthy eating habits need to be encouraged as early as possible but children should not be made to feel guilty about eating certain foods. There are no 'bad' foods but some are obviously better for us than others. Unfortunately, the sticky, sweet ones are often the most attractive. Encourage healthy eating by providing fruit or vegetable snacks on some days. Let the children help you to prepare them and talk about why the particular snacks have been chosen. Sort foods into sets such as crunchy or sticky, crisp or sweet and talk about how sticky, sweet ones stick to our teeth and may harm them, while crunchy ones, such as carrots, help to clean them and make them strong.

Taking exercise

Getting small children to run about and play is not usually a problem, the difficulty is more often in keeping them still! But

children are becoming more sedentary and they need to begin to appreciate why they need exercise. In exercising they also learn more about their bodies and what they can do. They become better at controlling their sometimes wayward arms and legs and learn new skills such as skipping and perhaps swimming. Learning to ride and control a bike is quite a skill and requires concentration and perseverance, but it's also great fun.

How do you grow?

At this stage in their lives children are growing and changing rapidly. Most will have photographs of themselves as small babies. Some may even have scans of themselves before they were born. Make a display of these photographs together with recent ones and talk about how they have changed. It is fun for all the adult helpers to bring in photographs of themselves as babies and see if the children can match the baby to the adult.

Ask children if they can find out:

❑ How long were they when they were born?

❑ How long or tall are they now?

❑ Why did we say 'long' when they were born but say 'tall' now?

❑ Are their feet still the same size?

❑ How did they tell people what they wanted?

❑ How do they tell them now?

❑ How did they move? How has that changed?

❑ Why didn't they eat chips when they were first born?

❑ What else can they do now that they couldn't before?

Most pre-school groups have access to at least one new baby during the year. If possible, invite mum (or dad) and baby in and do some of these comparisons together. This also provides an opportunity to talk about how babies need to be cared for and how we need to care for each other. Make sure that some of the questions are directed through the older brother or sister. It works wonders for self-esteem and may even help any pangs of jealousy that might be lurking.

This topic is often one that is done fairly early in the school year. If this is so, keep the height chart that you make and then compare the children's heights at the end of the year to see how they have changed.

Assessment

Children should be able to name the main parts of the body. Watch them as they join in finger rhymes or games such as 'Heads, shoulders, knees and toes'. Older children might be able to label a simple body picture.

Children should begin to understand that they have some responsibility for their own health. They should demonstrate that they know the importance of washing hands after using the toilet. They should know about cleaning their teeth regularly.

Stories

Bouncing, Hiding, Chatting, Giving Shirley Hughes (Walker).

All about Alice Penny Dale (Walker).

Faces Jan Pienkowski (Picture Puffin).

The Baby John Burningham (Red Fox).

Once There Were Giants Martin Waddell and Penny Dale (Walker).

Funny Bones Janet Ahlberg (Mammoth).

Something Special Nicola Moon Orchard Books.

Poems and songs

'Playdough People' by Tony Mitton, 'Last one Back' by Roger Stevens from *Playtime Rhymes* John Foster and Carol Thompson (OUP).

Poem for Ntombe Iayo from *Can I Buy a Slice of Sky?* edited by Grace Nichols (Blackie and Sons).

'Miss Polly had a Dolly' in *Okki-Tokki-Unga* (A & C Black).

Computer programs

Smart Alex: produced by Brilliant and available from Rickitt Educational Media (01458 253636) or Granada Learning.

People who help us

All in a day's work

There are elements of science and technology in all kinds of jobs, not just the obvious ones such as doctors. These activities focus on a selection of different occupations to give an idea of the potential this topic has for meeting all aspects of this area of learning.

The builder

Houses and homes

Almost every community will have a variety of different types of housing. Go for a walk and see how many you can see - houses, bungalows, flats. What other buildings are there in the area? What are they used for? Is there a community centre or village hall, a post office, a cinema, offices, a bank? What are they made from? Are they all the same? How were they built?

There may be some building work taking place somewhere close by. There are lots of health and safety issues related to building site visits so you may just have to view from a safe distance, but some firms may let you visit if you contact them well in advance. Take the opportunity to talk about the dangers of playing near building sites and how even the people working there have to be careful and wear special hats and boots to help keep them safe. You could perhaps borrow a hard hat and some safety boots to illustrate the point.

Look at a brick wall and see how the bricks have been laid. Can you see the pattern? Look at a different wall. Is the pattern the same? How many different patterns can you find? Use some thin paper and wax crayons to take rubbings from different walls. Use a fairly big piece of paper and stick it to the wall with masking tape or Blu-tack. Use the chunkiest crayons you have in fairly dark colours. Two or three children could work on each one. You may need to give a little help to make sure that the pattern of the bricks is fairly well defined. Stick the rubbings to big sheets of card and use them as pattern guides. If you stick them to the wall at floor level the children can match the bricks to the picture - providing, of course, that you have bricks or blocks of a suitable size,

Early Learning Goals

These activities will help you work towards all of the science and technology ELGs.

and build their wall up against the rubbing. In one nursery I visited, they had built a small brick wall, with the help of the caretaker, as part of their topic about 'The Three Little Pigs'.

Can you use the building bricks or blocks to build a wall in the same pattern? Can you make up a pattern of your own? How strong is your wall? Try rolling balls against the wall to see how easy it is to knock it down. Introduce the idea of fair testing by asking the children if they think it is fair to use different balls on different walls or to roll the ball from different starting points. Children will recognise unfairness long before they are able to plan for fairness in a test.

Hammer and nails

Apart from brick and slate, one of the other basic materials used in buildings is wood. (Where does wood come from?) Make a collection of objects made from wood. Go round the setting and look for all the things you can find made from wood.

What kind of tools do you need to make things from wood? Children can get great enjoyment from banging nails into a piece of wood and will go on for as long as your nerves can stand it! Such activities need fairly close supervision, but don't let that deter you. Make sure that you have the right tools. You can get small hammers that are not too heavy. A small, junior hacksaw will suffice for most things the children need to saw. Check the blades regularly to make sure they are still sharp. A small vice is useful to hold things steady and a small hand drill will enable them to make holes for wheels and axles. A strong pair of snips is a useful addition for cutting plastics or thin wire.

Before using them, sit all the children together and talk about the basic safety rules. Ask the children what they think they need to do to keep themselves

and other children safe. This helps them to think about risk and understand the part they have to play in keeping themselves and others safe. Some sources recommend that children should always wear protective goggles when hammering but I have had great difficulty in finding goggles small enough for pre-school children. Some of the softer varieties can be tightened sufficiently but they still tend to slip. I think that managing slipping goggles can distract children from the job in hand and finish up by being more dangerous.

I have never had a child cut themselves using a small hacksaw. Banged fingers can be avoided by using a clothes peg to hold the nail until it is started. You may be given off-cuts of wood from time to time. Check them carefully. Some of these are so hard that the children find it impossible to get a nail in or to saw through it and that is when frustration and bad behaviour can take over. Any wood you use needs to be fairly soft and of reasonable size. Don't expect the children to saw through a six-inch plank with a junior hacksaw! Sawing demands concentration and perseverance.

Hammering nails into a piece of wood is excellent practice for hand-eye co-ordination (and great fun). Try making a pattern with nails or tacks or the initial letter of your name. Many children will be content simply to do this. Older children may begin to make something that is vaguely recognisable, although don't be surprised if it starts off as a house and finishes up as a bus!

The garage mechanic

Try having a role-play corner outside in the better weather where customers can take their vehicles to be repaired. A few plastic tools will do little damage to bikes or scooters that can be taken to the garage to be 'adjusted'. You may have large construction toys from which the children can make their own

vehicles and machines or smaller kits that help children begin to think about how machines such as cranes and pulleys work.

At first the children will just want to play with the toy and explore its possibilities but as they progress and become familiar with the various components, set them specific tasks or simple problems to solve. Build the tallest tower you can; make a cart with four, six, eight wheels; use a pulley to lift a weight.

The postal worker

Most children will be familiar with Postman Pat and will probably have had birthday or celebration cards through the post. Some may have been lucky enough to receive a parcel. Did it arrive safely? How was it wrapped?

Think about sending a small gift to someone. How can we wrap it to make sure it arrives safely? Make a collection of packaging materials - brown paper, bubble wrap, Jiffy bag, string, sticky tape. With younger children the gift could be something fairly straightforward like a book or a scarf. Older children could consider how they might pack a small ornament or plate. How easily does the paper tear? What happens if it gets wet? Is it best to use sticky tape or string? Do we need to put the item in a box first? How can we stop it rattling around in the box?

Make your decisions and then, if you feel brave enough, try subjecting your parcel to some of the treatment it may get on its journey through the post. Stand the children in a line or circle to represent the various stages along the way. Stamp it at the counter and drop it in a bag. Put the bag on a trolley with other bags on top. Sprinkle lightly with a watering can. Unload it from the trolley and throw into another bag ready for the postman to deliver. How did your parcel arrive?

If you have a programmable toy such as a Pixie or something similar, then you could work out a simple route for the parcel van to take. Make a simple map on the floor. Either draw one out on a large sheet of card or use string and bricks to mark out a street or two. Make sure the roads are wide enough to accommodate the toy. Pretend the bricks are houses or offices and help the children to program the toy to stop at various points to deliver the mail.

The dentist

Most children will have made contact with a doctor and some may have seen a nurse or dentist. In many areas there will be a dental health authority that may supply packs and information for educational use. You may be able to arrange for someone to come in and talk to the children about brushing their teeth and eating the right sort of food to keep their teeth healthy.

Some private practitioners encourage young children to go and see the surgery and equipment so that a visit to the dentist becomes routine. It is worth making enquiries at your local dentist.

Doctors and nurses

Most home corners will turn into a hospital at some time during the year. A few children may have had a stay in hospital or been there to visit someone. Some may be willing to talk about their experiences while others may wish to forget the whole thing. Do be sensitive to the child's feelings and don't make them talk about it if they don't want to.

Take the opportunity to talk about the dangers of taking any pills or

medicines that they may find, or eating, drinking or sniffing any unknown substances. They need to know that some medicines are good for us but that some may be harmful.

Heart beat

Why do doctors sometimes use a stethoscope to listen to our hearts beating? What does a stethoscope do? You can buy a stethoscope for about £5. Children can use it in role-play situations but they may find it difficult to recognise their heart beats or chest sounds. It is not as easy as it looks! However, you can use a stethoscope to listen to a clock ticking or a key turning - something that will help the children to realise that all it does is to make sounds louder and it is not going to hurt. Have a small pot of disinfectant handy in which to dunk the ear pieces at regular intervals and withdraw it from play if you have any raging ear infections in the setting.

Children can often feel their own hearts beating by putting their hands gently on each side of their necks. They need to be still and quiet for a few moments but they should be able to feel it. Explain that this is their heart pumping blood all round their body so

that it can work properly. Now get them to run round the hall or playground and then stop and feel again. What differences do they notice? They may notice that they are out of breath or breathing harder. The pulse they feel in their necks should be much stronger and faster. Older children may have some ideas about why this happens.

Rubbish!

Older children might consider some of the people who work in all weathers to keep our environment clean and wholesome - the dustmen (or refuse collectors), road sweepers, the people who work at the council tip, the people who work in the sewers or incineration plants.

We all generate tons of rubbish each year that has to be disposed of somewhere. How can we help to make the environment better?

Which day do the bin men come? Where do they take the rubbish? What happens to it then? What would happen if they didn't come? Why is it important not to have piles of rubbish about?

How can we help? Encourage children to think about the things we throw away during a day. Make sure you have a 'clean' rubbish bin for them to sort. Never send children out to pick litter up from the environment for health and safety reasons. You can never be sure what they might find! In the bin that you make up, put things like empty drinks cans and bottles, newspaper, a cardboard box, plastic bag (make sure there are holes in the bottom - safety teaching point), an empty jam jar, apple core, banana skin and so on. Provide some gloves for children to use. Which of these things could we clean and use again? Which things could be made into something else? Which things would rot and make compost for the garden?

You may have a recycling point nearby where you could take your bag of rubbish and put the different things in the right containers. Some areas have recycling plants that allow visits.

Have a look round the school or local environment and see where litter collects. Is it in a particular corner or outside a certain shop? Would it help if there were a litter bin there? Is there one there already that isn't well used? Older children could write a letter to the council and suggest they put a bin there or they could make posters to remind people to put their rubbish in the bin and not drop it on the floor.

The crossing patrol

Road safety lessons can never begin too soon or be repeated too often. As with everything, if we understand the rules and the reasons for them then we are more likely to comply.

❑ Why does the lollipop lady (or man) wear a special coat?

Most crossing patrol people will happily come into a setting once their duties are finished and show the children their uniforms and lollipop. What is special about them?

Paint the inside of a shoe box black. Make a hole about as big as a 5p piece at one end. Make a similar hole in the lid but stick a flap of card over it so that it can easily be covered to cut out the light. Use a reflective armband or stick a small piece of reflective material, a piece of white card and a piece of dark coloured card to the inside of the box on the end opposite the hole. Put the lid on and, with the flap closed, what can you see? Open the flap a little and look again. What can you see now? What happens if you shine a torch through the top hole?

Why is the lollipop lady's coat white? Why does it have those reflective stripes? How does it help her to be seen better? Why is it a good idea to wear reflective armbands? Where else do you find reflective materials? Police, fire and ambulance workers all wear reflective clothing as well as many construction workers.

Assessment

Most children will realise that tools can help them and make some jobs easier. Look to see which children begin to choose the appropriate tools and the increasing dexterity with which they use them.

Through wrapping parcels or trying to knock their walls down, children will begin to understand that they can investigate or experiment with ideas. Watch for those children who start to ask questions of the 'What will happen if…?', 'How could you make…?' type. Some children will start to realise that tests should be fair and will recognise when they are not.

Stories

Rubbish Claire Llewellyn *Take one* series (Simon and Schuster).

Rubbish Sally Morgan (Wayland).

The Three Little Wolves and the Big, Bad Pig Eugene Trivizas and Helen Oxenbury (Mammoth).

The Big Concrete Lorry Shirley Hughes (Walker).

My Presents Rod Campbell (MacMillan Children's Books).

Traditional stories such as 'The Three Little Pigs', 'The House that Jack Built'.

Tools

Workbench/wooden tools available from TTS, Monk Road, Alfreton, Derbyshire DE55 7RL Tel: 01773 830255

Planning chart

Knowledge and understanding of the world	ELG 1	ELG 2	ELG 3	ELG 4	ELG 5	ELG 6	ELG 7
Pushing and pulling		✓	✓	✓	✓	✓	
What's cooking?	✓	✓	✓	✓		✓	✓
Growing plants		✓	✓				
Exploring the senses	✓						
Minibeasts	✓	✓	✓				
Sand, rocks and soil	✓	✓	✓	✓			
Investigating sound	✓	✓	✓	✓			✓
Amazing animals	✓	✓	✓				
Making puppets	✓	✓	✓	✓	✓	✓	
Electricity	✓	✓	✓	✓		✓	
Seasons: Science all year round	✓	✓	✓	✓	✓	✓	✓
Water: What can we do?	✓	✓	✓	✓			✓
Colour: Through the rainbow	✓	✓	✓	✓	✓	✓	✓
All about me: Who am I?	✓		✓				
People who help us: All in a day's work	✓	✓	✓	✓	✓	✓	✓